ASSET OPERATIONS

The Future of Maintenance, Reliability, and Operations

RYAN CHAN

CEO & FOUNDER OF UPKEEP

ISBN: 978-0-578-28780-5 (print)
ISBN: 978-0-578-28781-2 (ebook)

Printed in USA.
1 3 5 7 9 10 8 6 4 2

CONTENTS

ACKNOWLEDGMENTS

This book wouldn't be possible without contributions from the following people: Sean Flack, Matt Koprowski, Ashir Badami, Caitlyn Young-Gilbert, Chelsea Cho, Margot Ford, Dan Frohnen, Heather Grant, Vickie Valdez, Victoria Johnson, Vince Grosso, Pam Malinoski, Maryellen Cicione, the entire UpKeep team, all of our UpKeep customers, and those in The Maintenance Community.

A big thanks as well to the subject matter experts who contributed to and/ or reviewed this book: Ramesh Gulati, George Williams, Rob Kalwarowsky, April Johnson, Bob Latino, Ricky Smith, George Parada, LaWayne Smith, Luke Smaul, Radar Huntsinger, James Reyes-Picknell, Sarah Lukens, Michael Preston, Sanya Mathura, Markus Rimmele, Chris Colson, Susan Lubell, Matthew Moore, Florian Ferrier, Fabio Andre Brand, Mohd Nazly, "Joey" Hilard Ray Cantrell Jr., Evan Zabawski, Anna Goodman, Michael McKinney, Usman Mustafa Syed, Joseph Akpan, Joel Leonard, Roger Borycki, Paul Crocker, Padam Dev Singh, Ahmed Mazhar Bashir, AW Schultz, Rahul Sinha, Zibusiso Siziba, Dinu Ajikutira, Joshua Harris, Gary Rigdon, Douglas Plucknette, George Mahoney, Howard Penrose, Adam Napolitano, Rinae Musekene, Graham Immerman, Robert Gauna, James Kovacevic, Harvey Veenstra, Peter Funk, Joseph Sarullo, Jim Vantyghem, and Mike Miller.

Thank you to Ramon Carmona, Dave Brandle, Michael Moran, Fraser Campbell, Kyle Dunbar, and Chi Fang for allowing us to highlight their experiences within these pages.

And last but not least, everyone in the industry for supporting and sustaining our world; you're the unsung heroes.

PREFACE

It wasn't that long ago that many maintenance, reliability, and operations tasks were done by hand and recorded correspondingly. Employees were considered heroes for how quickly they reacted after an asset had broken down, as well as for the deep wells of knowledge that lived in their brains alone. Manufacturing plants would commonly wait until their equipment failed before making repairs.

The "hero" was the worker who stayed late to fix the issue; the one who scoured cabinets of paper files for insight into why the equipment broke down in the first place. These workers were forced to communicate through a hodge-podge of platforms: email, handwritten notes, and phone calls, and they did all of this for the good of the business without complaint. But then, the historical knowledge of a facility, its tips and tricks for assets—it all left when these workers transitioned or retired.

What elevates a maintenance, reliability, and operations worker to hero status shifts as technology changes the very landscape of the hero's journey. Today, equipment sensors can alert workers when repairs are needed. Heroes are commended for being quick, but today's quick is at the first sign of irregularity. The same workers who were praised for triaging in the past can now snap pictures of problems on-site, annotate, and submit maintenance requests—seamlessly updating all stakeholders live through their phones with just one message. And they're celebrated for it.

Reporting dashboards can pull up a full history of an asset's life cycle with just a few keystrokes, and the company heroes are the ones who ensure the right inputs are exactly where they need to be, so everyone can know what they know. Nothing is secret; they make sure of it. From this digitized knowledge, new employees can receive full, automatic templated instructions on their very first day. In our current world, there are more heroes than ever before, and they all get to go home earlier to their friends and families.

Let's look ahead. We still see the metaphorical compass pointing our industry toward further innovation. Workers will be able to utilize artificial intelligence and predictive analytics to prevent most mechanical breakdowns from happening in the first place. Driverless cars will own the road, and robots will do ninety percent of the manual work done in facilities, such as fulfillment centers to manage inventory and process orders.

If this inevitable evolution makes you fear for the hero's demise, you're not alone. I see dozens of headlines crowding news sites on how AI technology will completely take over the workforce—leaving maintenance, reliability, and operations workers unemployed and in the dust. These articles paint a world where an employee's traditional functions and contributions become obscure. The truth is, this fear is not baseless. Indeed, your current job in maintenance, reliability, and operations will inevitably be affected by the ongoing automation of tasks and digitization of information—perhaps so affected as to make your current role redundant.

The good news is, if the arc of history is any indication, you'll find yourself out of your current job and into an improved one—a better, higher paying, and safer one at that. In summation? Technology is going to change the scene forever, and the need for the company hero will always be there.

The long journey to automation has always brought with it three waves of change:

1. Make certain jobs redundant

2. Modify other jobs

3. Create tons of new opportunities we never before imagined possible.

Technology is, and always has been, a source of fear for many. But it's also been an exciting launchpad for most. Time and time again, "History shows that the economy has consistently adjusted to advancing technology by creating new employment opportunities and that these new jobs often require more skills and pay higher wages."[1]

There's no doubt that the job market for maintenance, reliability, and operations will look a lot different ten, twenty, or fifty years from now. New technologies are evolving the workforce and changing the hero's description, not replacing it. I know because I created some of that technology myself.

---

1   Ford, Martin. "The Rise of Robots: Impact on Unemployment and Inequality." *Confronting Dystopia: The New Technological Revolution and the Future of Work*, edited by Eva Paus, ILR Press, Ithaca, NY, 2018, p. 43.

When I was a 22-year-old engineer on the front-lines at a water purification plant, I saw firsthand how much clunky, outdated technology holds us back. I watched as technicians would spend most of their day in the field writing notes with pen and paper, return to the office, open their computers, and add an extra hour of work typing maintenance notes about the equipment before they could leave for the day.

Why was this the norm? Because for decades, software for tracking, predicting, and preventing equipment malfunctions was either expensive, difficult to use, or both. Technology wasn't keeping up with our industries' needs; we were slowing down to make it work for us. I wanted to introduce our industry to a game changer: reduce redundant work with easy-to-use asset management technology in the palm of employees' hands.

The first problem? The technology didn't exist. The second? I had no coding experience to create it. So I enrolled myself at the local community college and taught myself to code in three months while working full-time at the manufacturing plant. I wrote the first version of the UpKeep application from my mother's garage, all while funding the whole venture myself.

Today, this technology has unlocked insights, productivity, and revenue for over 3,000+ customers. The community of maintenance, reliability, and operations experts that advise us spans across 78 countries. And I'm not the only one putting money behind this idea anymore. Our technology has attracted some of the world's most preeminent investors including Emergence Capital, Insight Partners, and Y Combinator. To date, UpKeep has raised over $50M, and we're putting all of these resources behind creating technology that serves the maintenance, reliability, and operations hero.

The COVID-19 pandemic turned the spotlight on the maintenance, reliability, and operations hero's impact on the world at large. For the first time, public consciousness had to stop and consider how all facets of this community work together to keep life as we know it spinning. Our industries not only sustain huge sectors such as wastewater treatment and food manufacturing, but also keep families' homes safe and the local hospital functional. Not to mention conserving the road between the two. Now more than ever, governments, businesses, and communities are thinking about how to invest in the future of technology for our industries like never before. Our jobs are forever solidified into the category of essential.

Change can be intimidating, or it may even seem impossible, but change is also enabled by humans. It harnesses our existing knowledge, relies on us to course correct, and our creativity to build onto the next change to make the world better, safer, or more convenient. Like it or not, change is on the horizon—beckoning us toward a better tomorrow.

For automation to benefit the industry, this change will rely on you, the worker, to be its shepherd. "Computers and digital devices are doing for mental power what steam did for muscle power."[2] Why fear this shift, when you can be at the head of it, steering your company into revolutionary new levels of safety and profit?

In this book, I invite you to get ahead of the technology curve. Play an active role in your business today and in the years to come. In each section, you'll find real, tangible, step-by-step instructions on how to better your business using the tools and resources available to you today. We'll then discuss actions you can take to stay ahead of the technological transformations that will rock our industry through automation and the digitization of information.

Some of our ideas will be easily implemented at your business; others may take some time. But as we all know, a hero's journey always begins with a single step.

---

2   Paus, Eva. "The Future Isn't What it Used to Be." *Confronting Dystopia: The New Technological Revolution and the Future of Work*, edited by Eva Paus, ILR Press, Ithaca, NY, 2018, p. 6.

INTRODUCTION

In today's world, the majority of asset-intensive organizations are still stuck with complex, rigid, and sometimes antiquated technology solutions that simply cannot step up to evolving challenges and an ever-changing market.

Asset-intensive industries and organizations are those that rely on or manage facilities, equipment, and physical assets. Industries like manufacturing, agriculture, healthcare, and higher education are anchored by the performance of their facilities and/or assets. Companies operating in these spaces build teams around optimizing performance and preventing downtime.

However, these teams—maintenance, reliability, and operations—while essential to production, have been labeled "cost centers" and overlooked as key candidates for digital transformation. Industry 4.0, digital transformation, modernization, and the like have been part of the lexicon for a long time now, but certain industries like manufacturing have lagged in taking action.

Why do the world's most important industries—ones that billions of people rely on for essential human needs—operate with approaches that run the risk of making them extremely inefficient and brittle?

What if it didn't have to be that way?

Imagine a world where companies can move successfully into the future, where these brittle solutions are replaced with a flexible, simple approach that also delivers enterprise-grade capabilities.

This book introduces asset operations management (AOM), an operating principle founded on the belief that asset-intensive organizations have much to gain by adopting new approaches to data, collaboration, and communication—all supported by modern, consumer-grade technology experiences.

The best-of-breed organizations in these asset-intensive industries have been changing the way their businesses run for years, and they're reaping the rewards. The rest of the pack is struggling to keep up in the new paradigm—one where asset operations is central to operating efficiency and organizational resilience.

PART 1

Why Asset Operations Management

CHAPTER 1

WHERE ARE WE AND HOW DID WE GET HERE?

Today's maintenance, reliability, and operations teams are in a difficult spot. Despite being responsible for maintaining business-critical assets on a daily basis, these teams aren't treated like business-critical functions. Instead, they're viewed as cost centers—departments that simply consume resources and don't contribute to the overall business.

This can be seen in how maintenance, reliability, and operations teams are measured. They are measured by activity and not business outcomes. This fundamental difference can be expressed further in the following table.

Activity Metrics	Production & Profitability Metrics
Work orders completed	Decreased labor costs
Hours spent turning wrenches	Increased asset lifespan
Amount of preventive maintenance tasks completed	Reduced equipment downtime
	Increased efficiency and reliability
Percentage of preventive maintenance to corrective maintenance jobs completed	Overall equipment effectiveness
Hours spent in the field	Mean time between failures

The activity metrics on the left are all vanity metrics; they show what one's doing and not the impact they're making. These metrics also focus on maintenance utilization alone, not the language of the executive team and how that utilization is driving revenue and/or profitability. The end result is that this stereotype of maintenance, reliability, and operations teams being cost centers continues to be perpetuated. This stereotype is damaging for many reasons.

Maintenance, reliability, and operations teams are critical to improving business performance.

When these teams are working holistically and efficiently, they can:

- ► Increase production and output;

- ► Increase reliability;

- ► Impact profitability;

- ► Ensure resilience and compliance.

These teams aren't simply *turning wrenches* or *performing maintenance*; this is work that significantly contributes to better business outcomes.

Maintenance vs. Reliability vs. Operations

Throughout this book are references to three teams: maintenance, reliability, and operations. However, those names can mean different things to different people or organizations. Before going further, let's briefly outline how this book defines maintenance, reliability, and operations.

   Maintenance cares about repairs.

   Reliability cares about what's happening tomorrow.

   Operations cares about what's happening in the production facility right now.

Taking a Seat at the Revenue Table

The question then becomes: How can maintenance, reliability, and operations leaders get a seat at the revenue table? It's clear that something's missing; that current solutions aren't helping maintenance, reliability, and operations teams translate their technical language and metrics into executive language and metrics. This is a key point.

A solution that allows a maintenance team to *manage up* by linking its maintenance strategy and activities to the executive mindset and key performance indicators (KPIs) doesn't exist today because each team is thinking about its metrics and activities in isolation. Vendors have made this worse by catering to a siloed approach instead of trying to push for a unified system.

There are three ways these teams can earn that seat at the revenue table.

1. **Connecting the field to the office and boardroom:** Frontline workers need a digital solution that not only captures the work/activities they're doing, but also one that links their impact to business outcomes, such as asset health and performance.

2. **Utilizing technology that's easy to adopt:** A solution that workers want to use and will use on a sustained basis is key.

3. **Having a single source of truth:** If companies succeed in the previous two areas—where maintenance, reliability, and operations teams have the ability to connect all players, especially frontline active data creators, and make it easy to adopt—then can they create a repository of data.

When teams have all three of these, they can see holistically across different teams, spanning assets and activities. This expanded view allows businesses to make more informed business decisions on a complete picture. However, this has been hard to do, in large part because companies have disjointed systems—and as a result, disjointed practices—operating across these three separate teams.

Today, maintenance, reliability, and operations teams have access to more data than ever before. But something apparent across the market is that data isn't being shared across platforms and teams; it's fragmented across all the different systems. Despite working on the same asset in parallel, despite having the same intent, these teams operate separately. And what happens is each team's data lives in different places, is inaccessible, and is siloed.

So most teams are operating with inaccurate data that's also hard to get to. How can maintenance, reliability, and operations teams demonstrate that they have concrete business value if their processes and data are hindering them from the start?

The Impact of Disjointed Systems and Teams

A disjointed company culture has real consequences. The absence of accurate, accessible data leads maintenance, operations, and reliability teams to operate in a primarily reactive manner—and that leads to waste.

Lack of visibility: Seventy percent of companies lack awareness of when equipment is due for maintenance or upgrade, according to research conducted by GE Digital. Living on the edge all the time is not a sustainable way of life for a business.

Unplanned downtime: According to the *Plant Engineering* 2016 Maintenance Study, about 44% of all unscheduled equipment downtime results from aging equipment, making it the leading cause of unscheduled downtime. This is a huge competitive problem for companies. You might lose customers and have competitors swoop in to pick them up.

Wasted productivity: Factories can lose anywhere from 5% to 20% of productivity due to downtime.

The Three Key Challenges Maintenance, Reliability, and Operations Teams Face

Asset-intensive companies today find themselves at a crossroads: either continue working in misaligned and inefficient silos, or work holistically toward the same goals by leveraging technology advances and a new mindset. Unfortunately, many of these companies are traveling down the former path rather than the latter.

The problem might seem impossible to tackle, but three major hurdles demonstrate how teams got to this point.

Poor Adoption

One could apply the idea of poor adoption to any new software or initiative at a company, but it's particularly acute in asset-intensive industries and sectors where there are many desktop-oriented solutions: computerized maintenance management system (CMMS), enterprise asset management (EAM), and asset performance management (APM).

These traditional solutions are oriented for those who sit at a desk in front of a big screen. This is problematic because modern frontline teams who work on physical assets and equipment are out in the field and can't use these systems efficiently. That disconnect then becomes a point of friction, an irritation, and a deterrent to adoption. And if you have poor adoption, you have poor data.

Poor adoption is a big part of why data is in silos and why teams can't articulate a clear connection between their activities and overall business metrics.

Fragmented Information

Disjointed systems and disjointed teams equal fragmented information. Many companies today have data spread across all these different systems. The maintenance team is using a CMMS; the operations team is using an ERP or EAM, etc. Each system has its own wants and needs, and the team members are operating in their respective system. When information is so widely spread like this, it leads to difficulty accessing it. This scenario should be easy to imagine. "What's the right document? Where's the checklist? Is the checklist correct? What's the right workflow?"

Additionally, siloed data causes information gaps, which lead to rework. The UpKeep *State of Maintenance Report 2021* found that 20% of work done in the field is due to rework. Rework is work that is redone because the original job was done incorrectly. This is 20% of a company's productivity going down the drain.

But this isn't the technician's fault. It's because they don't have the right access to information to get it right the first time. If all of a company's data is inaccurate or hard to get to, then it makes consistent efforts toward working with accurate data difficult.

Poor Integration Between Systems

The third challenge is the actual technology. If you think of the monolithic ERP, CMMS, or EAM systems, they're not oriented toward end users and don't necessarily play nice with other systems. When one adds this to what's already been explained, then it's easy to see how problems start to escalate.

There are disjointed systems and disjointed teams, and now the systems are also not talking to each other. So, companies have pockets of data aggregating separately and not giving anyone in the business a unified view of what's happening. How can maintenance, reliability, and operations teams make a business case for impacting the bottom line if all these elements can't be integrated?

The Old Ways Are Simply Not Working

In addition to everything we've mentioned so far, every single team has different measures of success. Again, they're working on the same asset, but they're approaching the work with misaligned goals.

Everyone wants to improve the bottom line as much as possible, so why do teams work so independently to achieve this?

The technology companies have, the practices we utilize, the industry today—it's all been driven too much by a perspective focused on disparate systems and not a centralized or unified system that optimizes the business from an asset's perspective. Everyone has to start thinking about things differently.

CHAPTER 2

INTRODUCING ASSET OPERATIONS MANAGEMENT

All of this leads to a new category and mindset of Asset Operations Management (AOM). It's not just a technology solution; it's defining the future of maintenance, reliability, and operations. AOM is company-wide intelligence. It means threading together an organization's maintenance management, passive and active asset data, and unique operational processes to make it easier and faster for every employee to get what they need to do their jobs successfully.

An AOM solution isn't just a casual term; it's a very different shift in how a system works within a company. AOM is purpose-built to bring together all these teams and their data so they can *inform important business decisions*. In order to do that, teams have to have that full visibility across the entire life cycle. It doesn't matter if you're out in the field doing maintenance, you're just as important as the asset managers or executives in other departments.

It's every stakeholder unified under one system.

The Impact of Asset Operations Management

As mentioned before, organizational teams can be very tactical or oriented toward specific workflows. But in an AOM system, you're now combining cost, revenue, and asset data, making data easy to access, centralizing all the data, and unifying all these different dimensions so all these teams can work together to support business outcomes.

Unlike existing systems, AOM is less a feature set and more of an operating principle. The main tenets of AOM are ease of use, data consolidation, configurability, and the accessibility of enterprise-grade features for all company segmentations.

The system's implementation is designed to organically shift your culture and mindset—provided you commit. You'll move from a paradigm of interacting with an asset solely along the maintenance axis to thinking about the impact the asset's performance has on the business and how variations in asset and maintenance management can help shift business performance. In other words, it should help accelerate digital and organizational transformation toward greater resiliency, transparency, and flexibility, with data playing a pivotal role in making informed decisions that map to your business priorities.

AOM is meant to start you thinking about data differently, not just in terms of work orders and failures, but also about what a comprehensive health dashboard looks like. What does that dashboard look like for an executive vs. an operations leader? Suddenly, success shifts from thinking, "How much did I get done today" to "How much did that impact the business today?"

In this context, teams shift toward a mindset of thinking about the impact—the "so what" of their activities—versus trying to demonstrate being active to meet their activities-based KPIs.

	Team	Asset Interaction	Data	Success
BEFORE	Maintenance	Repair	Work Orders	Work Completed
	Operations	Production	Runtime	Downtime
	Reliability	Longevity	Failures	Availability

	Team	Asset Interaction	Data	Success
AFTER	Asset Operations	Entire asset life cycle	Comprehensive equipment health metrics	Business outcomes

Unlike traditional CMMS, EAM, or APM solutions, the AOM mindset has four key differentiators.

1. **Unifies maintenance, reliability, and operations:** An AOM solution brings data that traditionally lived in different software solutions into a single repository so it can be analyzed and leveraged to make decisions

that impact all three teams. Maintenance teams, for example, should be able to understand how reactive maintenance on an asset impacted monthly or quarterly revenue—not just see how many parts are stocked or how many work orders they completed in isolation.

2. **Is intuitive for every employee to use:** An AOM system prioritizes the quick and easy capture of data across passive and active data sources. Data quality and volume will suffer if adoption is poor, so ease of use is a top requirement.

3. **Creates a command center for data:** AOM consolidates data from across active and passive sources, as well as unifies data from maintenance, operations, and reliability. It links asset data to executive metrics so every team is aligned on the company's goals.

4. **Employs a cross-departmental approach:** Having a dynamic knowledge base for all teams increases cross-functional collaboration and communication. Integrating multiple systems and solutions is easier for workers instead of one system keeping them captive.

To help organizations find their way back onto a successful road to the future, they need a consolidated, robust perspective that brings together the strengths, tools, and data of maintenance, operations, and reliability. This is why AOM is a game changer for businesses.

AOM uses an interconnected approach that breaks down departmental silos, bridges the data and information gaps, and is purpose-built to support the mission of each department. The idea is intuitive for all employees and ensures the entire organization is moving in a single, concentrated direction when it comes to asset management. Unlike existing systems, AOM is less a feature set and more of an operating principle. The main tenets of AOM are ease of use, data consolidation, configurability, and the accessibility of enterprise-grade features for all company segmentations.

AOM provides maintenance, operations, and reliability with a single version of the truth when it comes to assets. This truth encompasses the entire life cycle, holds comprehensive equipment health metrics, and is measured by successful business outcomes. Again, it's about company-wide intelligence.

Let's take a look at how AOM specifically transforms maintenance, reliability, and operations teams. Assume an organization is ready to adopt an AOM strategy, preparing to pull together its technician services, passive and active data, and company-specific operational blueprint to make it simple and seamless for all employees to get the information they require to perform their duties successfully.

How AOM Will Transform Maintenance Teams

Although a company might be utilizing a CMMS system, many technicians still find it somewhat cumbersome and difficult, primarily due to the fact that interaction must take place through a desktop computer. Top technicians try their best to obtain needed information before heading out to the field, as well as enter comprehensive details for each work order completed. But more lax technicians tend to skip a few details in favor of completing the work order and heading home for the day.

Unfortunately, this scenario is fairly typical. According to the *State of Maintenance Report 2021* conducted by UpKeep, roughly fifty-nine percent of those who use an integrated CMMS/ERP system report that their software is difficult to use. At the same time, about one-third of the industry still said they are using pen and paper, spreadsheets, or nothing at all to manage their company's maintenance activities.

AOM, on the other hand, is user-led and focused on putting tools readily at hand to encourage adoption throughout a manufacturing company. It also directly affects and benefits maintenance teams in four specific areas:

Easier Work Management

AOM is one centralized command center for your maintenance team. Having one centralized command center allows an organization to drive accountability, streamline workflows, and utilize maintenance data. It also acts as a dynamic knowledge base—a source of truth across fragmented resources that eliminates information silos and connects teams across departments and locations.

By grouping an organization's fragmented systems, workers can quickly locate answers without constantly switching between platforms. The goal is to achieve a unified view of everything—assets, teams, schedules, devices—all creating data and insights that ultimately lead to easier work management.

AOM also uses mobile interfaces that can travel with technicians whenever and wherever they work. This makes it much easier for maintenance technicians to complete and report on tasks. As a result, the speed, quality, and responsiveness of the work increases. Also, since AOM groups and organizes all data from fragmented systems and makes it accessible from one location, technicians can quickly find answers to questions without logging into and out of multiple systems.

Deeper Reporting and Analytics

Data is at the center of maintenance with AOM. Teams can use the platform to analyze asset performance and optimize long-term efficiency over an asset's lifetime. Real-time performance data, coupled with remote condition sensor data, also allows maintenance teams to understand critical business metrics

Once data is unsiloed, teams can receive granular data on each interaction to find ways to enhance and optimize performance. Maintenance teams can easily create comprehensive reports, build their own dashboards, and leverage all the data the team generates to gain essential insights.

The next generation of maintenance will come from collecting the right data, displaying the best insights, and providing actionable feedback. AOM gives maintenance teams this opportunity.

Better Use of Resources

The asset operations data collected across different channels synthesizes to show insights and drive work efficiency. This data can then be used to prioritize and direct efforts to tasks that actually matter. It changes the conversation from "How many hours did you work today?" to "This is the value you've added to the business today." AOM brings departments together to better execute preventive maintenance programs, which reduces equipment downtime and helps assets achieve their full useful life.

Additionally, if a work order requires a part that is out of stock, it can be ordered immediately and the work order updated to be placed back in the queue once the part is available. If further investigation or questions arise, technicians have the means to immediately text or contact a supervisor or flag the issue for further review. If the work can be completed, any notes, questions, or other data can be immediately recorded and available within the system for anyone else in the organization to access in real time.

From an individual standpoint, technicians are freed from non-value-added tasks, such as searching for the right information, which allows them to spend their time on more critically important issues. From an organizational standpoint, AOM allows automatic load balancing, which examines both the existing volume of work orders and technician availability and workload.

Greater Visibility and Control

AOM provides a complete picture of all work orders performed with nothing falling through the cracks. Not only does this optimize overall service, but also workload balance. Teams are able to automatically load balance tasks based on existing volume and be their most productive.

All equipment instruction guides, manufacturing checklists, maintenance history, parts inventory, and work order requests are available from one simple interface. When technicians arrive at a work request location, they can immediately pull up a work order that tells them who requested the work, what needs to be done in detail, and possibly photos of the issue. They can also see the last repair or maintenance record, how frequently repairs have been requested, illustrations and instruction guides about the problem, and other information that can help streamline the task.

AOM represents a new approach to how organizations become more reliable, efficient, and adept at making informed decisions. This new approach is built with maintenance teams in mind, and is coupled with an affordable, easy-to-use, and flexible solution.

With AOM, maintenance teams can be seen as a revenue generator instead of a cost center. It's a mobile-first experience that gets buy-in for the platform from day one.

How AOM Will Transform Reliability Teams

The reliability team is an integral part of the company. Its mission is to stay on top of and manage all reliability issues, maximize plant facility uptime, and ensure company safety protocols are met.

While mega manufacturers can afford to invest in sophisticated, complex asset performance management products, some companies simply do not have the resources to do so. AOM can be a viable alternative as it focuses on simply mainstreaming the ideas of APM, as well as supervisory control and data acquisition (SCADA) and the Internet of Things (IoT), for all types and sizes of businesses. By doing so, AOM can help reliability teams stay ahead of those preventive maintenance tasks that can reduce downtime. In addition, AOM can increase both the speed and quality of responsiveness to routine facility questions through automation and artificial intelligence.

For example, when routine maintenance tasks are requested at an organization, they are automatically routed to more entry-level technicians. However, if a complex equipment situation arises, those tasks are sent to seasoned employees.

For reliability teams, AOM drives accountability, streamlines workflows to reduce menial tasks, and allows workers to focus on the important issues. All of these benefits change how reliability is reported in order to shift how reliability is valued.

Improved Reliability

AOM allows organizations to get ahead of preventive maintenance, ensuring uptime and increasing the speed and quality of responsiveness to routine facility questions. These results are possible by ensuring tools, operations, and people cohesively work together toward the same goals. When disparate systems become aligned, reliability teams are able to make important business decisions with full visibility across the entire company life cycle.

Additionally, through standardization and automation of preventive maintenance tasks, reliability teams can increase the lifespan of their assets and avoid catastrophic failures—key objectives for any reliability team.

Automated Issue Assignment

Managing a reliability department can be overwhelming, especially if you have an immense number of assets and technicians to oversee. With AOM, tasks can be automatically assigned to appropriate team members with the correct expertise. Additionally, AOM guarantees consistency with work order documentation and instant access to work order information.

Automation benefits extend beyond work assignment tasks. AOM continuously tracks each employee interaction, whether it be a technician or a reliability engineer, within a facility. This eliminates the need for employees to manually log each step within the process and also ensures asset records are kept completely up-to-date and accurate.

This is particularly valuable when managers and executives routinely log into the system's reporting and analytics capabilities to find areas for continuous improvement and new opportunities to optimize the performance of the organization. Maintenance, reliability, or other internal teams can also access an accurate picture of the status of work orders to obtain updates and ensure no details are left unaddressed.

Reduced Paperwork

Technology is moving at a breakneck pace. However, many reliability teams are still managing tasks with pen and paper systems. Whether it's word-of-mouth, phone calls, emails, or sticky notes, these inefficient tactics significantly weaken productivity and increase costs.

AOM continuously tracks interactions within a facility versus employees having to manually log each step. This platform is designed to streamline work orders, collect maintenance data on labor and assets, manage inventory, and generate reports that can lead to long-term, smarter business decisions. It's one front door for team members to get what they need.

Greater Visibility and Control

We're currently living in an intelligence golden age. Despite this fact, many reliability teams aren't utilizing technology advances. By utilizing AOM, reliability leaders receive granular data on each interaction to find ways to enhance and optimize performance.

Some possibilities include:

- ▶ Custom dashboards that align with your reliability team's metrics and KPIs;

- ▶ Visual and PDF reports for any premade or custom dashboard for easy sharing throughout the organization;

- ▶ The ability to categorize and view work order statuses by technician, team, asset, or location.

Reliability teams get a complete picture of all work orders performed, ensuring nothing falls through the cracks, to optimize overall service and workload balance.

Traceability and Audit Trail

Making sure an organization is compliant with regulatory standards is an integral part of a reliability team's duties. AOM automatically logs and tracks each item in a facility for any and all regulatory/compliance needs. Users can provide historical documentation and upload safety and regulatory manuals so workers have the information they need.

Furthermore, AOM provides configurable analytics and reporting so inspectors and regulators have all the historical information they need. Since this complete and accurate record is updated continuously, data is always available for recalls, regulatory compliance, or internal or external audits.

For example, in the United States, companies in the health care sector must always be acutely aware of data rules around the Health Insurance Portability and Accountability Act (HIPAA), designed to protect individual medical records and identifiable data. Within the food and beverage industries, regulations around the Safe Quality Food Program and the Global Food Safety Initiative must be followed and documented. These and many other evolving state and national regulations require a myriad of data in order for organizations to be compliant.

AOM also changes how reliability-related tasks are reported, which leads to a transformation of how reliability is valued. This means increased accountability and more efficient workflows, which help all employees reduce menial tasks and focus on those issues critical to maximizing uptime.

How AOM Will Transform Operations Teams

Nearly midway into 2022 and there are still no real solutions to help operations teams link asset, maintenance, and reliability data/intelligence to executive metrics like revenue, cash conservation, margin, etc.

A company might have a CMMS, EAM, or more, but these traditional systems don't link team-specific metrics to the broader business goals. With application silos and hard-to-use software abound, operations are forced into a reactive state and cannot connect the field to the boardroom. This lack of integration and direction slows operations teams, hampering them with manual tasks and unnecessary errors instead of propelling them to the next level of success and growth.

An AOM mindset, on the other hand, targets the pain points that have thus far prevented operations teams from achieving a unified view of their individual contributions toward supporting business performance. Among those pain points are ease-of-use to drive adoption and engagement, centralization and accessibility of data, and data-driven support.

When we think about operations teams being better supported, valued and understood, AOM becomes even more critical. It's clear from the following benefits that AOM offers an operations team one blueprint for their company with efficient workflows and the visibility to improve workplace operations.

Strengthened Resource Allocation

One of the core pillars of AOM is the idea of data flowing into a central command center. This single data repository can also be a dynamic knowledge base that removes information silos and connects teams. Once this streamlined data goes into effect, workers are applied to where they're needed most, maximizing systems in the most effective ways to further the organization's goals and KPIs.

Improved Speed of Service

When assets, teams, schedules, devices, and more are aligned, the speed and quality of responses are increased, giving operations teams the efficiency they need to make better decisions. Employees are also able to get convenient and immediate help within the tools they're already using through a conversational omnichannel experience. Even routine answers are automated with AI-driven ticketing.

Technicians perform at the top of their skill set, and talent and experience are not wasted on tasks that can be completed by entry-level employees learning the ropes. This helps maximize all resources across the entire company, furthering the organization's performance and helping it meet goals and key performance indicators. AOM isn't just a one-time occurrence; it's purpose-built to bring teams together and foster a culture of efficiency and visibility.

One Operational Blueprint for Efficient Operations

AOM drives accountability and streamlines workflows to reduce an operations team's workload. Every work order is accounted for with visibility and real-time updates. Plus, with standardized workflows, opaque processes in your operations department are eliminated.

The paradigm shift of AOM also removes obstacles that hinder assets from getting proactive maintenance, thus allowing team members to plan their work and be their most productive. The analytics from every interaction provides the visibility teams need to improve and accelerate operations across the entire organization.

Visibility, Reporting, and Analytics

Operations teams have access to more IoT, ERP, and technical data than ever before; however, this data is still siloed, and users aren't able to unlock its full potential. Additionally, most workflows aren't standardized or documented, so operations employees have to learn by trial and error or asking colleagues.

The AOM data collected across different teams synthesizes to show operational insights on performance, efficiency, revenue generation, cost savings, and more. Operations teams get granular data on each interaction to assist with enhancing and optimizing performance. This data can also be used to create detailed reports, personalized dashboards, and essential insights.

Better Asset Management

A regular preventive maintenance plan can be initiated with AOM, which reduces equipment downtime and achieves the full useful life of assets. AOM also anticipates replacement parts needed based on actual condition of the asset (feedback from PMs or based on condition from CBM analysis), and management can get real-time notifications of part quantities.

Additionally, AOM is integrated with a company's tech stack for a central knowledge base to connect fragmented systems and assets. Operations teams can access their asset information and history from anywhere.

Why It's Time to Embrace AOM

Given the disjointed, inefficient state of many asset-intensive companies today and the ever-changing global economic landscape, it's an opportune time to pull the efforts of maintenance, reliability, and operations together. Each has made incredible individual strides over the years. Now, it's time to get all three disparate groups pulling in the same direction for each and every asset.

With its holistic, company-wide view, AOM is an affordable technology that delivers the same powerful capabilities as costly, enterprise-grade solutions. It can unify these disparate departments, solving a myriad of problems currently plaguing asset-intensive companies.

By threading together a company's technician services, passive and active data, and unique operational blueprint, AOM makes it easier and faster for every employee to get what they need to do their jobs successfully in a coordinated and aligned manner.

Today's teams must be proactive, flexible, and ready for unexpected events. AOM gives an organization an all-important unified front that's stronger and more resilient for today's business environment.

PART 2

The Eight Pillars
of
Asset Operations

This section outlines the eight pillars of asset operations.

1 Maintenance, Reliability, and Operations Operate Together and Align on Achieving a Common Goal

2 Data Must Flow Into a Single Repository

3 Measure Teams Based on Why They Do Something Rather Than What They Do

4 Collect the Right Data, Display the Best Insights, and Provide Actionable Feedback Through a Centralized Command Center

5 Continuous Improvement as an Abundant Life Cycle, Not Just a Point in Time

6 Everything Measured Can Be Improved

7 Data Accessible From Wherever You Are

8 Maintenance, Reliability, and Operations Are Revenue Drivers, Not Cost Centers

These are the core ideas behind the larger concept, and they'll provide a better understanding of what asset operations truly encompasses.

Throughout Part 2, we've enlisted various subject matter experts to give their thoughts on AOM-related topics. Their contributions have the heading *State of the Industry*.

CHAPTER 3

MAINTENANCE, RELIABILITY, AND OPERATIONS OPERATE TOGETHER AND ALIGN ON ACHIEVING A COMMON GOAL

Imagine a world where maintenance, reliability, and operations teams operate together and are aligned on achieving a common goal. What would that look like? For one, it would mean no more infighting between the three teams about when to take a piece of equipment offline, when to run scheduled maintenance, when to run a piece of equipment to failure, or what production goals should be.

It would mean complete alignment between maintenance, reliability, and operations, so each team can focus on what they do best. When teams are synced like this, it enables them to run at full speed 100% of the time. But it's not just teams who would benefit; it's the whole organization. Companies would operate more productively because pointless meetings would be gone.

It's a world where maintenance, reliability, and operations teams aren't stuck in pointless meetings, worrying about politics. Everyone would all come together to achieve one common goal; one unified team where everyone is there to help each other. Some more benefits include: lower cost of goods, more reliable equipment, less human error and safety issues, better working environments, and happier people.

It can be hard, though, to get workers on the same page initially. Natgas, a Mexican company dedicated to promoting an environmentally-friendly fuel alternative, used work order data to create a motivational, competitive game for its employees. Not only did technicians see how they compared with colleagues, but they had an opportunity to earn extra vacation days for good performance.

Ricardo Andre Carmona, Director of Engineering at Natgas, explained that he extracted work order data and began sharing it on a daily basis by posting pictures of the technicians on company televisions, along with how many work orders they had opened and closed over the last week, as well as how many work orders they had active.

"Beyond that, I could start grabbing the data and create a really interesting scoring system," Ricardo said. "If technicians completed work orders on time, they got 100 points. As the deadline passed, the points earned would drop. They could see their scores in progress, and the person who had the highest score received an extra day off the next month. The whole team was really into it."

EVERYTHING WITHIN AN ORGANIZATION SHOULD BE SYNCHRONIZED.

-RICKY SMITH

This core concept of AOM revolves around bringing together the maintenance, reliability, and operations teams to rally around the same goals for each and every critical asset. It's a mindset, a culture, a philosophy that must be supported by the right data, technology, and tools to make it happen.

What would it look like if organizations weren't split into disjointed, siloed teams? Natgas is a great example. Let's go back to them.

A Better Future

During some of Natgas' initial growth, their maintenance efforts were being handled by individual technicians in varying ways. Some technicians would perform work orders and put them in binders, while others would use a spreadsheet or a CMMS system that was in development. Ricardo knew he needed to bring all these elements together and to connect the maintenance system to the company's other systems.

Without a centralized repository of data, each of the three key asset-focused teams at Natgas would be working with incomplete information, at best, and heading off in a completely wrong or extremely inefficient direction at worst. Once Ricardo and Natgas settled on an AOM mindset and solution, it helped everyone involved to jump-start Natgas' ability to deep dive into existing data.

Additionally, the connection between systems and teams helped the company spot other inefficiencies. About the mindset shift, Ricardo said: "Our dashboard allows us to see how our electrical consumption is tied to maintenance efforts. We had one situation where I noticed that we had a sudden increase in electrical consumption, and I could see that we happened to have maintenance work done by a contractor during that same period.

"I asked my manager to check into that immediately, and we discovered there was some modification that one of our contractors had made on our equipment that caused the increase. It was spotted so quickly, and that incident alone saved us 20% of our electrical bill per year."

Another of the company's goals was to reduce the amount of corrective maintenance, which was at about 50% before AOM. As teams collected more data, workers had what they needed to make smarter business decisions, and management could get a better overview of all the stations and what was happening in terms of equipment and components. After AOM, Natgas reduced their corrective maintenance to 20%.

Another benefit of having maintenance, reliability, and operations aligned on a common goal is the increase in productivity. Technical teams could get together proactively to check meters and graphs for different assets in different locations. These teams could say, "All right, we're good here" and move to the next location or identify something as a unified team that needed more attention.

The Impact of Disjointed Systems and Teams

Let's say a hypothetical food and beverage manufacturer continues down the alternative path for another five years. Equipment continues to age. Maintenance, reliability, and operations work harder every year to meet their departmental goals. Critical assets remain in the middle, at the hands of multiple team members pulling them in somewhat different directions. Over time, this disjointed scenario will begin to negatively impact each of the three departments involved, as well as the company as a whole.

A maintenance team could see its balance shifting from preventive maintenance tasks to more reactive ones. Stress levels for technicians begin to rise and more of them start to feel like they are always "putting out fires." Managers and operators submitting repair requests are seeing the maintenance staff negatively as they blame them for broken equipment and increased downtime.

Maintenance costs begin to skyrocket, reinforcing an age-old belief that maintenance is a necessary evil and unavoidable cost center.

Meanwhile, the operations team can no longer boost uptime with band-aid fixes and begins to experience a domino effect through the facility. Unplanned downtime rises, resulting in lost production and unusable labor.

At the same time, consumer demand for more natural and organic ingredients, as well as shorter delivery time frames, put additional pressure on the organization. While the reliability team struggles with having enough resources to keep the aging equipment running around the clock, it also faces difficulty in tying its work to business finances in order to justify funding additional support.

Suddenly, the company begins to miss deadlines for order deliveries and sees an increase in back order issues. Customers start to complain about late and incomplete shipments due to production issues. Costs rise while market share and profits begin a downward slide.

The AOM Solution

If, however, a company chooses to embrace the asset operations management philosophy before heading down this typical path, it can avoid many of these negative impacts and reap the benefits of its maintenance, operations, and reliability teams united around asset-focused goals. Let's take a look at this alternative scenario again and its resulting returns.

When the food and beverage manufacturer hits its 10-year anniversary, the management team recognizes the need for an integrated, centralized system that can pull all its asset-related data into one centralized repository. It knows it needs a cultural change as well as a realignment of company goals around asset health.

Management leads the effort, working with departments to redefine goals and objectives away from the work being done to revolve around the value being provided. Maintenance begins to reward technicians for problem-solving, adding value to the process, and flagging underlying issues instead of simply completing and closing work orders.

At the same time, a technology solution that centralizes data is put in place so when a technician is assigned a work order for a repair, a detailed explanation of the current problem with photos appears. The complete history of the asset, including all preventive maintenance performed, all problems and repairs reported and completed, any failure modes discovered by reliability, all manufacturer documentation, relevant checklists, and the status of parts within inventory is at the technician's fingertips. By combining all this data with the technician's own past experience, they're empowered to complete the repair, make a temporary fix while flagging another expert for a closer look, or get additional assistance or parts as needed. The technician has all the tools and data to do the right thing each and every time.

WHEN PEOPLE KNOW THE SCORE, REFLECTED WITH CONSISTENT, ACCURATE DATA, THEY ARE ABLE TO MAKE BETTER DAILY DECISIONS.

-RICKY SMITH

The operations team has ready access to standardized and documented workflows, which eliminates trial and error efforts and searching for answers by calling or emailing colleagues. A customized dashboard allows the operations team to obtain operational insights on performance, efficiency, revenue generation, and cost savings, all in real time. The new asset operations solution anticipates replacement parts needed, updating the management team on part quantities and order status, as well as their effects on outstanding work orders.

Since the reliability team now has access to granular data on each work order, the team can now enhance and optimize the performance of each asset. This work and its results are easily organized and presented as dashboards that align with KPIs in formats such as shareable PDFs and customizable reports. Any member of the organization can have the ability to categorize and view work orders by technician, team, asset, or location to discover more opportunities for reliability improvements.

STATE OF THE INDUSTRY

Ricky Smith
Maintenance Expert in Residence | *UpKeep*

Organizations that are reactive in their approach to maintenance, reliability, and operations are dysfunctional. Companies should operate as one team, focusing on the same goals. That means if a problem arises, everyone works together to solve the problem. We can't continue to work in disjointed or dysfunctional ways.

For example, most reactive organizations have maintenance in one spot, and then operations somewhere else. These organizations also don't hold regular scheduling meetings. Teams might have maintenance scheduling, but operations never shows up to those meetings. Why? Because the teams don't see the value, further strengthening the dysfunction.

Additionally, many of these reactive companies lack documented procedures. If a company doesn't have procedures, it doesn't have specifications. Everything within an organization should be synchronized. If you want to reduce human-induced error, you have to have formal procedures, planning, and scheduling.

To combat these issues, teams must ensure they have a fully functional mobile solution and that people use it. Sometimes when I go to an organization and start looking at its data, I'm like, "You don't even have the assets in the asset registry." How are we going to manage the assets if we don't even have them there?

It's like trying to drive from New York City to San Francisco in seven days. It's possible, but if you don't have waypoints along the way, aren't checking your gas gauge or GPS, and aren't ensuring you're hitting the targets, you'll never make it.

The only way a company is going to get out of this reactive mindset is by admitting it has a problem. If not, the good people will leave and the bad people will stay. I see it all the time. There's usually one good leader in an organization, but when they get to the final point and can't do or change anything, they have to go work someplace else. Then, all these people that work in the plant and want things to go well see this serious leader leaving and morale gets really bad.

If you're really working toward the same goals, then it makes it a lot easier. Focus on the same goals and have scorecards. When you're driving an organization, there ought to be a large scorecard or dashboard on display. Not what you did yesterday; what I care about is where you are right now. What does the map look like? What's the data?

When clear goals are established and a company's teams know what actions are needed, sharing ongoing processes through a dashboard is an excellent way to make sure everyone "knows the score." Such a tool is an easy way to motivate a team as well as pull everyone together toward the goal of improving performance. Everyone will want to see the scoreboard and understand how they are doing individually, as a team, or as an organization.

Let's take a look at an example of creating a maintenance dashboard. In order to set up an effective maintenance dashboard, you'll need to measure maintenance processes to optimize asset reliability at optimal cost. Begin by identifying the steps in the maintenance process, from preventive maintenance (PM) and predictive maintenance (PdM) through your failure reporting, analysis, and corrective action system. This may include work identification, planning, scheduling, work execution, work order closeout, and failure reporting.

Once those requirements are met, select KPIs that are related to where your company is currently functioning, as well as your goal. For example, if you're mostly reactive and you're trying to move to PM, you should be measuring KPIs like percentage of planned work and PM compliance. However, if you're already doing preventive maintenance and trying to move to PdM, you should be measuring things like defects found in PdM inspections and number of PdM work orders executed.

A planner may go back into the system and pull a random number of work orders to see if they are closed accurately. Be sure to identify the metric used in each step and post to the maintenance dashboard for specific audiences.

A dashboard can help a team understand if it is using the company's resources effectively, including specific players in an organization. As a result, a maintenance dashboard should be posted where everyone can see it. Maintenance score dashboards should tell a story, good or bad. When people know the score, reflected with consistent, accurate data, they are able to make better daily decisions.

For instance, it's critical that work orders are closed out correctly. Thus, a supervisor should review the work order, and a planner should close the order to ensure it's not done haphazardly in the middle of other pressing priorities for the day. This can help ensure the data going into your system is accurate, clean, and usable for the future.

Be sure to set high standards for your organization. World-class standards may seem unreachable but strive for them anyway. In world-class organizations, costs are low, overtime is low, production delays are low, and production output is high. On the other hand, worst-in-class companies struggle with high maintenance and overtime costs, as well as production delays and low output levels.

Consider how much your maintenance, reliability, and operations process impacts cost, output, and quality. Look at your maintenance cost as a percentage of replacement asset value. Remember that this is industry, operations, and equipment specific. Where do you sit? How can you move in the right direction?

Start with production and what it requires. You have to start with the endgame. Determine things like rate, pressure, overall equipment effectiveness, availability, throughput, and cost. As we continue the process, reliability engineers ensure all asset reliability meets full functional requirements. The maintenance team must maintain equipment to those specifications with repeatable procedures.

One final important aspect when it comes to alignment is the Certified Maintenance & Reliability Professional (CMRP) and Certified Maintenance & Reliability Technician (CMRT) certifications. If management becomes CMRP certified, but the technicians aren't CMRT certified, then they're not aligned because those certifications are aligned. Many people miss that. Sure, technicians know what they're doing, but are they certified?

CHAPTER 4

DATA MUST FLOW INTO A SINGLE REPOSITORY

In order for an organization to successfully embrace and implement asset operations management, it needs to find a way to redirect and streamline data into a centralized location. In most companies today, data becomes siloed in different departments and technologies, making it nearly impossible to uncover a single source of truth.

How Data Silos Are Created

No business tries to purposely create data silos; they are often a result of rapid IT implementation and departmental goals. Data silos do not cause as many problems for smaller organizations since the owner and key management tend to have a better handle on the details of their business. The problem becomes more significant as companies grow and more team members need to contribute to and access the increasing body of data.

Sometimes, companies are entirely made up of trusted employees, where all team members have a great deal of autonomy and license to make the decisions deemed necessary as the company grows. Teams and departments start to form, and if a manager feels a certain technology was necessary to make the company operate more efficiently, there is freedom for decentralized purchasing decisions.

A few years down the road, this company might merge with another small family business that had created a complementary product to quickly expand its market share. Now, multiple data silos exist, resulting from the rapid growth and the merger.

Where Data is Siloed

Data silos can exist in a wide variety of areas, especially in a fast-growing start-up. First, a great deal of information probably exists in the minds of the original founder and team members. As they were getting the company off the ground, they most likely purchased and repaired what they needed as almost an afterthought as they scrambled to meet customer orders and build their business. Initial communication about any repairs or maintenance may have taken place as team members passed one another in the hallway or on sticky notes posted on someone's computer.

As the company grows and adds more product lines and functions, this "system" may graduate to phone calls, text messages, and emails—none of which are usually captured in any centralized way. At some point, the organization reaches a moment when it knows a more organized approach is required and may move to spreadsheets, a stand-alone app, or a CMMS, ERP, or EAM system.

While incomplete and trapped data is a big part of the problem in creating data silos, another issue revolves around the behaviors of different departments. Maintenance, operations, and reliability all tend to measure what they do in order to justify their roles and jobs within a company—instead of the value they bring to the critical asset themselves. This attitude can lead to collecting and using only specific data points, which may or may not be telling an accurate overall story. The refocusing on better, more comprehensive metrics is a key factor in implementing an asset operations management philosophy.

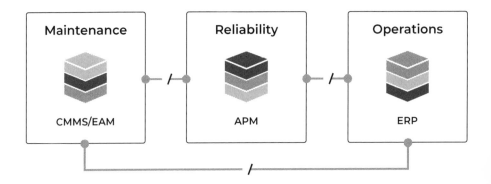

Why Data Silos Are Problematic

As companies grow and add different apps and software, it begins collecting duplicate information about equipment and recording it in multiple places. This eventually leads to a great deal of manual work, as well as duplicate data saved in an inconsistent manner across different systems. Employees trying to make decisions based on the data are not confident about its accuracy and sometimes, senior technicians "know" in their own minds and based on personal experience, that something seemed "off" with particular reports. As a result, "data-driven decisions" really don't exist. Rather, experienced individuals go off gut instinct, trying to make the best decisions based on what they know to be true.

Although this method may work for some time, once a company grows large enough and needs to hire outside professionals to help move the company forward, the system quickly breaks down. Now, siloed data that is disjointed, incomplete, and inaccurate paints an inconsistent picture for these new technicians or managers, leaving them handicapped in making the best decisions for the organization moving forward. This problem can be further exacerbated when regulatory and compliance requires accurate data to meet reporting requirements, causing stressful audits and potential violation fines.

How AOM Breaks Down Data Silos

By embracing an asset operations management mindset, employees can operate more as a single team. Previously isolated data can now feed into a central command center. This streamlined data gives the teams the ability to focus on the optimization of assets across the entire life cycle while also acting as a dynamic knowledge base. Now, not only can all employees pull necessary data from this centralized system, but they can also contribute to it. This single source of truth pulls together fragmented resources, eliminates data silos, and connects teams across departments and locations.

One key aspect of AOM implementation is the underlying cultural change that must take place among the employees. All members must buy into the necessity of the change, understanding why it's critical to not only for the future of the company, but also for the success of their department and their individual careers. The management team should invest time and resources to communicate the "what's in it for me?" message from the beginning, as well as created well-publicized dashboards, competitions, and gamification of asset-focused metrics. As small successes are reached, these should be widely communicated so that employees could readily see results quickly and regularly.

YOU'RE FOSTERING AN ENVIRONMENT WHERE PEOPLE ARE ABLE TO GIVE FEEDBACK ON WHAT'S WORKING OR NOT WORKING, WITHOUT A FEAR OF REPRISAL.

-ROB KALWAROWSKY

Benefits of Single Data Repository

Once a company gets its single data repository established with all team members using and contributing to this centralized source of truth, the organization quickly begins to see results.

First, since the data was more complete, executives can see more consistency between the information and what they knew to be true. This increases the level of trust in the AOM data repository and is a motivating factor for these team members to build and contribute to it.

Over time, metrics are redefined to focus on the life cycle and health of each critical asset, helping maintenance, operations, and reliability all zero in on the same goals. Instead of measuring, reporting, and being rewarded for the activity itself, the company, departments, and individuals are all considering how their activities were adding overall value.

This leads to a visible increase in productivity as equipment becomes more reliable. Repairs and maintenance are performed correctly the first time because all history, checklists, and background information are readily available, resulting in a decrease in rework and emergency repairs. A business could now clearly see the overall performance of critical assets and make good decisions about repair and replacement.

In the end, customers receive promised quality products and services on time, leading to a high customer satisfaction rating, a loyal customer base, and increased profits and continued growth.

Better Inventory Management Means Faster Repairs

Managing maintenance for 1,500 machines is complicated in and of itself, but it becomes even more complicated when you don't know whether you have replacement parts in stock, or if you do, where they're located. Before implementing AOM, Layfield Group Limited, a company dedicated to providing construction materials, packaging solutions, and medical products, had trouble keeping track of parts in an organized manner.

"Now, any of my guys can pull their phone or tablet out and see what we have for inventory," said Dave Brandle, facilities and safety manager at Layfield Group Limited. "They no longer have to check the spare parts bin. We have parts cabinets specific to each machine, so when a machine breaks down, we can quickly check if we have the right part, send a work order, and get the machine fixed right away."

Being able to manage parts through a single repository saves Layfield Group Limited thousands of dollars in lost time. It gets the company up and running in ten minutes versus someone running around trying to figure out if they have the part. That same individual might run all over the factory for an hour or two trying to find a part that's not there. In two minutes, he can find the part number, availability, and location."

STATE OF THE INDUSTRY

Rob Kalwarowsky

High-Performance Leadership Coach | *Elite High Performance*

A lot of what we do now in management and leadership comes from Frederick Taylor, who wrote the book, *The Principles of Scientific Management*, in the early

1900s. So it's a lot about industrial efficiency; it's a lot about making sure each task is as efficient as possible. And so for that efficiency, when you're thinking about it in terms of an assembly line, you're trying to optimize each person doing one specific thing. That's why companies would create silos because they want you to get really good at, say, turning a bolt.

A lot of what we talk about now in leadership is this term called VUCA, which stands for volatility, uncertainty, complexity, and ambiguity. That's more where our businesses today are at. We talk about it more like a VUCA world because we've changed much from this very standard level of manufacturing to how we create value today, by innovating, thought, and continuous improvement. And for that, you need a lot of different leadership styles than you did in the past.

Maintenance, reliability, and operations operating together and aligning to a common goal is everything. What we see often is maintenance is at odds with operations, and reliability sits on the sidelines, or sometimes they're at odds with both. But really, every company needs to be aligned in every department toward the vision. In 2022, people are talking about how it's the year of purpose-driven work, so companies have to have a bigger meaning than just "We want to make more money." And that's really where Gen Z comes in. They're the first group of people who say purpose, meaning, and all these things are more valuable than money and benefits. So, we need to cater to that as leaders because if we want to track talent and retain it, it's more than just "Hey, here's another 10 grand a year."

And that's the piece that often falls apart in a lot of the industries I've worked in. For example, "safety is number one." Literally, every company and all their customers—you'll see it on the door, on a sign, on their website. Yet, when it comes down to projects, are we going to do this one project that's going to make us more money or the one that's going to increase safety? Often it's the one that goes through production or profitability, and that's when you destroy those moments of trust and become an inauthentic leader.

There's a piece of this, too, which is motivation. And what a lot of companies do—it's where the fear-based motivation comes from—it's all extrinsic. If you do well, we give you more money or a promotion. If you don't do well, we fire you or yell at you. But on the opposite side of that, if you have a why that's bigger than money, or you have a vision for a better world, it's intrinsic and pulls you to do your job in the best way. And it also gives you meaning as a person. Extrinsic motivation works only so well; it keeps having to get bigger. Whereas intrinsically, people go to work and they're engaged, happy, high-performing, and they come home and bring that to their families.

So it starts with alignment. You have to set the foundation of trust and ensure you have a lot of psychological safety, so you're fostering an environment where people are able to give feedback on what's working or not working, without a fear of reprisal. These are the ways that you can actually implement something that'll stick versus people just looking for reasons why it won't work and telling you why it's not working.

Maintenance, reliability, and operations are always going to be seen as a cost center by accountants, at least, and a lot of CEOs or executives. These people have an accounting background, so they're going to see it as a cost. This is the hardest part. It's about putting benefits forward, talking about what you're doing, and the benefits of doing this long-term. To be honest, a lot of it also comes down to the executive's ability to see past today. It's incredibly hard to say, "I did some predictive maintenance, and in an alternate universe where I didn't do that, this thing blows up and we lose a million dollars." Somebody has to actually believe you when you say that.

But all they're seeing is, "Well, so-and-so cost $500 today, and the PdM machine cost $5,000, and the training cost $3,000, but everything's working." So it's about communicating wins, talking about the why you do things, and educating. But also leaders need to be open to the conversation. We saw this during the COVID-19 pandemic. What was the first thing companies did? They cut contractors, consultants, staff, and wages, while other companies leaned into their staff, started training them up, and that's why the latter companies saw results and the former didn't hit their goals.

A lot of those in the industry struggle with their beliefs about the impact they can make, and sometimes leaders aren't ready to take the journey to learn about themselves and how they can be a better leader. And there's nothing we can do about that. You can take a horse to water, but you can't force it to drink.

Daniel Goleman has this book called *Emotional Intelligence*, and in it, he has a model for leadership that says leaders need to be self-aware first, then they can be emotionally intelligent. It basically means, I have an emotion, I can understand it, then I can change it to what I want to feel, then you can become empathetic. After becoming empathetic, one can be relationally intelligent, which means, "Now I know what our relationship is like, and how I can inform and make it better." But before we get to that and to empathy, which are the true aspects of leadership, we have to go through ourselves.

CHAPTER 5

MEASURE TEAMS BASED ON WHY THEY DO SOMETHING RATHER THAN WHAT THEY DO

The old saying in business that "you can't improve what you don't measure" can be modified in today's competitive environment to say that "you can't improve the right things if you measure the wrong things." Many manufacturing companies frequently measure activity instead of value, which forms the basis for the third AOM pillar.

What would it mean if teams weren't measured just based on the number of work orders completed or hours that they worked, but instead how they impacted the bottom line?

How would it affect businesses? Every single business could be more profitable and make smarter business decisions. Teams looking at why they do something rather than what they do would completely change maintenance, reliability, and operations teams.

Among the many challenges companies across the country deal with are a labor shortage and high turnover. At the same time, the demand for maintenance workers is projected to grow by up to 8% over the next ten years, according to the U.S. Bureau of Labor Statistics.

However, according to a study by Deloitte and The Manufacturing Institute, as many as 2.1 million manufacturing jobs in the U.S. will be unfilled through 2030. Furthermore, employees say it's 36% harder to find talent in 2022 than in 2018. And finally, according to the U.S. Bureau of Labor Statistics, voluntary attrition rates are as high as 25%. Can you imagine turning over your entire workforce every four years? That's what's happening right now.

Shifting the mindset would help get more individuals excited about the industry, and it would change the perception of this societal role that we oftentimes don't value as much as we should. Let's dive deeper into the difference between what and why, and why this is an essential distinction.

The Difference Between the What and the Why

To illustrate this concept, let's take a fictional agricultural business. This organization is capital-intensive, requiring expensive farming equipment as well as hefty overhead and labor expenses to deliver a quality crop to the market. In order to keep its assets up and running, particularly during the busy harvesting seasons, the company wants to measure and improve the performance and reliability of its equipment.

However, like many asset-intensive businesses, this agricultural company uses metrics such as number of work orders, hours turning wrenches in the field, the number of preventive maintenance orders that were completed, and the percentage of corrective jobs that were done. Maintenance technicians are compensated and rewarded for performance against these metrics. However, these types of measurements look at what employees are doing, considering only the activities themselves and not the value that they do or don't bring to the organization.

Wrong Focus Leads to Undervalued, Undersupported Employees

At many companies, there's a significant disconnect between what's being rewarded at the technician level and what's being valued at the management level.

If the maintenance manager sits down with a team of technicians and focuses on the number of work orders completed for the week, that sends a clear message that closing work orders successfully is the goal. As technicians head to the shop floor or out to the field, they carry their work orders for the day with the goal of completing as many as possible.

Let's drill down further and look at one technician's specific workday. Say, Joe, has three years of experience and is a skilled and reliable technician on his company's most critical assets. He pulls up his work orders for the day and heads to a grain grinder that is malfunctioning. He scans the equipment, finds the culprit, repairs it, and closes the work order. However, due to this narrow focus, Joe does not perform any level of inspection or basic maintenance, even though he had to disassemble part of the equipment to make the repair. As a result, the machine will likely malfunction in another month, opening another work order.

The operations team is concerned about the downtime associated with the grain grinder, seeing that it seems to fail regularly. Reliability has some of the same concerns and plans to look for root causes of failure. Meanwhile, the management team sees the maintenance costs associated with the piece of equipment and wonders how the company can continue absorbing high maintenance overhead while staying on top of production.

This disconnect may lead to operations and management looking for ways to reduce costs by decreasing the number of technicians that maintenance can employ or postponing the investment of mobile technologies to make tracking of repairs more efficient. Joe and the other technicians, in turn, become frustrated with increasingly high demands with less support and fewer rewards.

EDUCATE PEOPLE ON HOW THEY IMPACT THE OVERALL OPERATION OF A PLANT IN EACH ONE OF THEIR DEPARTMENTS, AND MEASURE THOSE THINGS BASED ON BEHAVIORS.

-GEORGE WILLIAMS

How AOM Makes a Difference

The third pillar of AOM shifts this mindset from measuring the "what" to the "why." If a company makes the shift, its team will begin looking at metrics such as the amount labor costs decrease, the overall equipment effectiveness, the increase in asset lifespan, and the increase in reliability of each critical asset. All three teams of maintenance, operations, and reliability begin working together on the asset itself instead of against one another.

First and foremost, AOM requires a shift in mindset and culture. As an organization, employees must turn their focus to managing the entire life cycle of an asset. More comprehensive data metrics are required, all team members must have access to a single source of truth, and success must be measured by business outcomes.

Let's return to the previous example and look at what such a shift in mindset means in practice. Now, when the maintenance manager meets with a team of technicians, the message is that they must ensure that assets are running effectively and efficiently. The number of work orders is no longer the goal; instead, the team will be rewarded and recognized for improving the overall equipment effectiveness and increasing the life span of critical assets. In order to do so, an integrated, mobile AOM solution is implemented to provide a single source of comprehensive truth for all team members to focus on this new asset-specific goal.

Now, when Joe heads out to that malfunctioning grain grinder, he first reviews the history of repairs and sees that a technician has had to fix the equipment several times over the last year. He skims the manufacturer's recommended maintenance checklist and glances over common troubleshooting information. Once he arrives on site, he begins to disassemble the equipment to make the repair. While he's working on the asset, he inspects other parts and performs some preventive maintenance tasks. He also notices that another piece of equipment is sitting in close proximity that's causing a great deal of vibration near the grinder. He snaps a photo and tags the reliability team for a closer look. In addition, there seems to be an unusual noise as the grinder turns on and off. Although it's not causing any immediate problems, Joe makes a note and tags a more senior-level technician, asking for advice.

As other maintenance technicians, reliability engineers, operations management, and others rally around the assets themselves, the company begins to realize business results that directly affect its bottom line. No longer is the maintenance department seen as only a cost center, but rather a true partner in generating revenue and results that come with optimizing all critical assets. All employees feel valued and supported, building overall company morale and fueling even greater improvement and change for the future.

Pinpointing the Root Cause of a Problem

At FMLY, a property management company, Technical Director Fraser Campbell admits that change is difficult for everyone. Even his own maintenance teams had some initial challenges with the introduction of AOM. But, Fraser recognized the importance of positioning the new AOM initiative as an ally.

"Most of the maintenance technicians had almost a free hand to run things as they thought best before we came into the picture, albeit with limited budgets," Fraser said. "I think their noses were a bit out of joint in the beginning because they thought it was going to tell them what to do and control them."

Fraser kept reminding the teams that AOM was going to give them the evidence to resolve problems the way they wanted to do and fix things properly. However, as the data developed, team members started coming around.

"It showed us the time and money we had spent patching over issues with low-cost solutions instead of properly fixing them, and that the short-term cost increase to fix issues properly lowered the cost of maintenance in the future, which gave the maintenance team the backup they needed to prove their points to the hotel management company and free up budgets to find permanent solutions. Now, everyone sees the benefit."

In addition, Fraser explained that many of their clients' properties had been conventionally focused on operational issues and providing the best customer-service possible, and facilities management was not seen as an important element to their success. Although the guest experience is certainly important, FMLY has proved how critical a data driven maintenance-focused arm is to their operations, especially critical in Edinburgh where many of the existing buildings FMLY manages are hundreds of years old and therefore present unique challenges.

STATE OF THE INDUSTRY

George Williams
Founder & CEO | *ReliabilityX*

I would say a vast majority of organizations work in disconnected silos, and I don't think they do so through an active desire to be in silos. I think it happens naturally through the structure of goals and how they're disseminated throughout an organization. What I mean is, the organizational objectives are interpreted differently inside individualized departments with no understanding of the inner relationship of how that department impacts the reliable operations of the plant.

For example, let's say a company has an objective to reduce their cost of goods sold by two cents. And somebody in procurement decides they can buy less expensive boxes, so they negotiate less than ideal specifications on the boxes, which means the company can cut larger stacks and save a penny. So inside procurement, they're celebrating. "I found the penny; we're awesome!" But the impact that has to plant operations is suddenly a bunch of box jams inside the plant floor. And procurement doesn't tell anybody they're buying less expensive boxes, or how they got them less expensive; they simply do it.

If this company creates millions of units a year, you don't realize the impact of just a one minute stoppage every hour, and what that impact is to the business. Say you're operating at 100 units a minute; that's millions of units a year. Operations is getting dinged because they're not hitting their orders, because no one is interrelating the purchasing goal to the operational goal. Everyone should own the operational goal and the value delivery of the asset first—everyone. After that, you then get individualized goals. So, if operations isn't hitting what it needs, that has to come first, and people should get training in how they interrelate and individually impact the value proposition of the equipment and assets.

In order for these silos to get broken away, you need shared objectives. If you start to understand the goals and who impacts the goals, you can create these shared metrics. Educate people on how they impact the overall operation of a plant in each one of their departments, and measure those things based on behaviors.

A majority of the organizations we look at fudge their overall equipment effectiveness (OEE) number to look really good. But when we assess their plant, they're running somewhere around 50% to 60% OEE, and they'll continue to do that in a siloed environment until organizational discipline is created in the operation and sharing is done on how the operation succeeds. Nobody's trying to mess up the operation, but they're doing it nonetheless.

Operating together and aligning on a common goal is important for a lot of reasons, but I think it reaches far beyond just the common goal piece. You can have a common goal that's misinterpreted. Like the example with the boxes and procurement interpreting reduced costs as good. That's a common goal in a lot of manufacturing companies. The problem is, no one started a company to cut costs. You started a business to serve a need and be profitable.

It's very difficult to be effective, operate effectively, and create revenue, and it's harder than being a critic. Being a critic is easy—finding waste, criticizing it, and making it go away is easy. That doesn't mean you operate more effectively. You can do the wrong thing very well.

So what tends to happen is an organization running at 60% OEE no longer has the profitability it used to have. I'll give you a better math scenario. You produce a million units a year, and at a million units a year, your cost is X. Some of that's fixed cost, some of it is variable cost. If you now produce 60% of that, your cost per unit goes up. If cost per unit goes up, then profit goes down.

But that's not how companies interpret that goal. They interpret the goal to find a way to reduce cost, so they buy cheaper bags; they cut corners. They figure out a way to cut costs when that's not actually the goal. The goal is to be more profitable. So understanding what the entire organization's objectives are and breaking down silos is a necessity toward effectively operating.

I think in connecting people's everyday work, whether it's in pharma or gag gifts, there's got to be a why, and connecting what people do every day to the why is really important.

The hardest thing in any plan to do is create organizational discipline. You see people create shadow boards and they hang up their tools. Why is that a thing? The answer you'll get for most organizations is so that everything's back in its place, people know where it is, and they don't have to waste time finding it. But that is not why the shadow board exists; it exists for organizational discipline. If you can't put a broom back, how are you going to do the rest?

The initiative, 5S, creates organizational discipline. If you want to know how successful a company will be at your initiative, go find the shadow board they put up in 1998. If it doesn't have anything hanging on it, ask them why it wasn't sustained. That's the hardest part. People don't take the organizational discipline part seriously enough, but it's the driver of every successful initiative. Companies that have diligently created processes and training around those processes will have a much easier transition than organizations that have not.

For maintenance, reliability, and operations teams to be seen as a revenue driver and not a cost center, companies need to look at things in a new light, not rewarding cost-cutting or firefighting mentalities. Organizations need training on how to articulate things back to the business. Here's an example: I'm working with a company that is trying to get funding for a very baseline initiative, something like collecting my asset hierarchy. There's not really an immediate dollar value back to the business for this, right? And so, team members ask for a couple hundred thousand dollars to collect tens of thousands of assets. What do you think the company's response to that is? "That's great. We don't have $200K to pay for that. It's not worth my time."

When we were walking through the plant, we came across a machine that glues labels onto a bottle. And consistently, this machine would attach a label to one of the rotating plates, which meant the operator had to stop it and spend time to scrape a label off that got glued to its own plate. We watched this for 25 minutes. For 25 minutes, the operator struggled, finally shutting the line down and fixing the problem. It took 25 minutes of downtime for a unit that produces 300 units a minute. 300 units a minute, almost 30 minutes of downtime, and it happens every day, all day long.

My recommendation back to them, to this individual that was taking us on this tour, was to calculate what that looks like annually. Let's say it happens once a week. That's thousands and thousands of units a year. The reason you don't know this is a problem is because you can't track the problems when they call maintenance out to assets.

So, I can start giving you data or would you like to keep running like this?

CHAPTER 6

COLLECT THE RIGHT DATA, DISPLAY THE BEST INSIGHTS, AND PROVIDE ACTIONABLE FEEDBACK THROUGH A CENTRALIZED COMMAND CENTER

A common theme in maintenance, manufacturing, business and even life in general is the fact that there is simply too much disorganized data out there. According to *Statista*, the total amount of data created, captured, copied, and consumed globally was around 64.2 zettabytes in 2020, projected to grow to more than 180 zettabytes by 2025.

Although more data is being collected and juggled every day, much of this information is completely useless unless companies can access accurate, targeted information in the moments they need it in order to make smart, informed decisions. For asset-intensive organizations, this means relentlessly collecting the right data, creating a single source of truth for and from all parties, displaying the best insights to the right people, and providing actionable insights that drive better business decisions. That forms AOM's fourth pillar.

When a company has the right data, they can get into this virtuous life cycle of constant, continuous improvement. Because it's not *just* about collecting data, displaying insights, and driving actions—companies need to complete this loop over and over again. It means the rate of change, the rate of improvement is going to get increasingly, exponentially better. And we'll start to increase the pace of innovation.

If companies committed to these three actions, it could change the world in ways none of us even know. When businesses start making decisions based on data from actionable insights, the possibilities are endless. It's a loop, a life cycle loop that accelerates the pace of innovation across the entire business. That's what collecting the right data, displaying the best insights, and providing actionable feedback does.

Let's explore this pillar through the lens of a fictional manufacturer that produces components for heating and air conditioning systems. Although this company has an excellent reputation for producing quality parts, it has experienced growing global competitive pressure over the last decade. In addition, supply chain issues have made sourcing necessary materials more difficult than ever, affecting the company's ability to deliver on existing orders in a timely manner. The organization is struggling with attracting and retaining employees with the right skills and training; existing team members often feel undervalued and undersupported in a highly stressful and demanding production environment.

Data Issues Contribute to Problem

For years, this manufacturer has used an ERP system as well as a CMMS solution to manage its business. The CMMS solution holds the majority of asset information, but because there is no mobile access, reports and analytics data usually reflect last month's activity and results.

Very little data collection is automated; the company relies on its technicians and managers to input information as part of their job duties. A great deal of manual work is required by various team members to ensure data is entered properly and, in some cases, moved between disconnected systems correctly. This is an onerous and time-consuming process that often gets overlooked for emergencies or higher priority tasks. Entering data is seen as "paperwork that can be done later" by the vast majority of busy team members, which leads to gaps and oversight in the data collection process.

In addition, maintenance, operations, and reliability teams frequently work with siloed information, seeing their segment of the world through a narrow lens. Because of the lack of real-time information and an underlying distrust of data quality, team members frequently inject a fair amount of gut instinct and personal experience into decision-making. This often leads to inefficiency, stressful emergency repairs, and a culture of overtime and underappreciation.

IF WE WANT PEOPLE TO ACCOMPLISH A METRIC, THEY SHOULD BE PART OF DEVELOPING IT.

-BOB LATINO

AOM Prioritizes Collecting the Right Data

One of the key pillars of asset operations management is relentlessly collecting the right data into a central repository so that all team members working with the asset have a single source of truth. This can be accomplished through both passive and active data collection.

One of the first things that this manufacturer decides to do on its AOM implementation journey is to install strategically placed sensors on critical assets to continuously monitor performance and send alerts as soon as particular data points fall out of acceptable ranges. All this data can be collected passively and without human intervention, which leads to a highly efficient and accurate collection of real-time information. Not only can the maintenance team be alerted before major failures or breakdowns occur, but passive data helps build the all-important historic information on assets that can be used in predictive models down the road.

The company then works to improve its active data collection process, which requires employees interacting with assets to enter and record critical data. Because basic data is being collected passively, technicians are freed from mundane manual data collection and can focus on more complex issues and problems. An AOM system that makes it easy for technicians to upload pictures of relevant issues, reach out to colleagues who are experts in different areas, and empower employees to truly add value to the asset management process provides the support that team members need to improve the active data collection process.

All employees who work with assets should be invested in creating a complete and accurate data file for that asset as they do their daily work. Then, this can be utilized later by all to truly add value and make a positive business-related impact.

AOM Data Collection in Practice

Let's look at a fabrication machine as an example of data collection. The company's CMMS does contain manufacturer documentation, including recommended maintenance and equipment limits and capacity. Over the years, perhaps 70 percent of work orders have been reasonably entered, albeit not always containing enough detail. Replacement part information is stuck in the company's ERP system, which can lead to long lead times when repairs are necessary. No passive data collection exists.

As the company moves to an AOM system, a central data repository is created, which contains all the information related to that particular fabricator. The new software integrates with existing technologies, streamlining the flow of all existing data into a central data lake that can provide comprehensive and complete asset information. Sensors that monitor things like vibration are installed and passive information is collected, feeding this data into the central repository on an ongoing basis.

Once both passive and active data collection systems are in place, the company can begin applying predictive models and algorithms to that data, which can then be used to drive various workflow engines that will lead to business-focused improvements and results.

The richer the data, the better predictive models can do their jobs. Built on years of historical findings, experiences and data, predictive models can help define what and when work needs to be done using a workflow engine for each critical asset.

In the fabrication machine example, this company can use predictive models to analyze data that is constantly being updated on this asset. Perhaps significant performance differences occur after certain maintenance is performed or a similar repair request appears every quarter, generating curious patterns that can be pulled out and shared with the reliability team. As that team explores root causes of failures and makes needed adjustments, the predictive model incorporates that data into the central asset file, generating real-time reports for the operations team on current productivity levels. In the meantime, maintenance technicians continue to make and record repairs and preventive maintenance activities, which are constantly updated to improve the asset's overall performance and extend its life cycle.

Each time this cycle is repeated, the data becomes richer and the business sees improvement in machine performance, a significant reduction in unplanned downtime, and a boost in revenue generation.

History of Repairs Helps Improve Design of Future Coffee Shops

In the southwest, where a certain coffee shop is currently expanding quickly, the company is able to look at work orders from existing stores to guide designs of future ones.

Some of their stores were built within the last year, and they can see which work orders came up in that first year. Managers can talk with their construction team and ask if they can just tweak this design or build this part a bit differently, so they avoid future similar work orders in any new store.

For example, the design of the floor drainage system is critical for the company to manage all the waste from coffee machines and milk products. Previously, they had placed the plumbing that led to the floor drain near the area where employees store a rolling ice bin. Baristas frequently came into that area and bumped the bin or pipe, causing it to break and leak.

Employees could show the construction team the actual work orders and photos of what was happening. In their new stores, they've had that plumbing moved to a location under a sink where nothing is stored to avoid those types of work orders in the future.

STATE OF THE INDUSTRY

Bob Latino
Principal | *Prelical Solutions, LLC.*

Oftentimes, companies operate in disconnected silos because each team has a different focus. Maintenance are the fixers, reliability is the consistency of the operation, and operations are the moneymakers who get first-quality products out the door in a timely manner. However, in today's connected world, we can no longer be competitive operating in such silos.

As we move forward in this technology era, the human element will come more and more into focus as critical to the success of any organization. New technologies and analytics will only be as good as their developers and users. Human performance will become just as critical (if not more) as asset performance. We will recognize that the competitive edge will be the decision-making skills of our workforces. Uncertainty is the enemy of reliability, and this creates an environment for the unexpected to breed.

The concept in this book of AOM focuses on putting the information necessary to improve decision-making at the fingertips of those that need it now. Most poor decisions are made due to either having less than adequate or non-existent information, or from not having enough time to make an informed decision. AOM changes this in an effort to raise the bar on decision-making skills, and hence, field performance.

Few go to work in the morning looking forward to doing a bad job. We all want to be viewed as skilled in our craft, especially in the eyes of our peers and our families. This is where we make our living and where we spend a 1/3 of our life. Why wouldn't we want to look forward to ways to make the work more interesting, challenging, creative, efficient, safe, and profitable? This is what human reliability is all about, understanding how to support people as individuals, so they can do the best job they possibly can for the company. Most do not understand that human reasoning is a key element of a holistic reliability approach.

An example of how our organizational systems may fail us is when we find out failures in the field were caused by defective parts. When analyzed in a subsequent root cause analysis (RCA), we find that purchasing agents were buying less expensive parts (not like-for-like). Why? Because their incentives encouraged that behavior in order to get their bonuses. They responded as the system design intended. This is not their fault; it's the organizational system design's fault.

Unfortunately, few are correlating that maintenance costs are going up while purchasing agents are getting bonuses. These sleepers often go undetected for years. Usually a failure has to occur, an RCA done, and then these types of system causes are uncovered.

As an organization, we all have unity in purpose. We want our companies to succeed as well as ourselves and co-workers. We want to put out a quality product for a fair price. We want to do all of this in a safe manner. One of our primary goals must be that everyone goes home unharmed, just like they came to work. Safety plays a critical role in these departments: maintenance, reliability, and operations. Studies demonstrate there is a correlation between safety and reliability, so the more reliable we operate, the safer our people will be.

My career has been spent in reliability, but with a specialty in RCA. Inevitably, there are going to be people who have made an error or omission in their decision-making. But when an organization says they're doing an RCA and it concludes with blaming a decision-maker, they are not doing RCA . . . they are superficially doing Shallow Cause Analysis (SCA).

Organizations that practice SCA can plan on repeat failures because they've failed to understand the systems that failed their decision-makers. True RCA is not interested in who made the poor decision, but why they thought it was the right decision at the time.

When we dig down—and I don't care which discipline you're talking about—it's usually not the humans that cause the undesirable outcomes. They're usually the victims of our deficient systems—systems that did not provide either the adequate or accurate information to make the proper decision.

When such effective systems are in place, as this book suggests, then the key is that they should be institutionalized. This is a fancy word for indicating that the success of any initiative should not be reliant on an individual, champion, or sponsor. Effective leadership will ensure the systems put in place survive the creators of those systems when they depart.

When my father was running a Corporate R&D Reliability Center in the '70s, he tried to change the name of the maintenance and reliability departments to 'Terotechnology Departments.' According to Wikipedia, it involves the reliability and maintainability of physical equipment regarding installation, operation, maintenance, or replacement. Decisions are influenced by feedback throughout the life cycle of a project. So this is confirming that the focus of both departments is on the life cycle of the asset. A lot of people wonder where the overlap is between maintenance, reliability, and operations—and there is overlap—they're all strictly interdependent on each other.

While I have a bias, the reliability department has the most difficult task in justifying their existence. This is because they are one of the rare organizations whose effectiveness is measured by something that didn't happen. However, while reliability is not a revenue stream per se, its effectiveness can easily be measured by cost avoidance. When we become truly reliable, there are fewer unexpected failures, and the monies set aside in the budget to address them are now freed up to pursue true opportunities.

In my view, maintenance addresses today issues and reliability addresses tomorrow issues. For this reason, maintenance leans toward becoming efficient at reaction, and reliability folks are focused on proaction.

I'd like to note that contrary to popular belief, holistic forms of RCA can be applied to proactive opportunities. While RCA is most known for analyzing undesirable outcomes in hindsight, when using systems like AOM, the same RCA methods can be applied to why risks are unacceptably high. The sign of an exemplary RCA effort will be that a certain percentage of analyses are on proactive opportunities.

I do a lot of RCA work, and it's amazing to me the amount of people who do RCA and don't involve the field. In my view, if you're not involving the field, it's Shallow Cause Analysis, not RCA. When we don't involve the field, we often find ourselves putting words in peoples' mouths. We find ourselves making statements like, "He made that decision because of XXX." That's dangerous and hypocritical. Unfortunately, we tend to judge others based on the outcomes of their decisions, yet we prefer to be judged by the intent of our own decisions. True RCA is about understanding the intent of the decision-makers!

In our professions, we can all unite in defeating the following paradigm (a paraphrase of W. Edwards Deming, I believe):

> *"We NEVER seem to have the time and budget to do things right, but we ALWAYS seem to have the time and budget to do them again!"*

CHAPTER 7

CONTINUOUS IMPROVEMENT AS AN ABUNDANT LIFE CYCLE, NOT JUST A POINT IN TIME

Calling AOM an abundant life cycle means it's a continuous life cycle of constant improvement. No longer are you looking at equipment simply as a depreciating asset that has a 10-year life span. Instead, you are looking at your assets like critical revenue drivers that have this dynamic life to them. Suddenly, you have the ability to decide whether it's going to last five, ten, or even twenty years. And then, you can start applying a revenue model based on the dynamic life span the asset has—based on how you treat it.

This idea can significantly impact businesses. Currently, they purchase assets, put them into a depreciation schedule with a fixed lifetime, and then replace them. But imagine a world where you hold the keys and control that life of an asset. It would completely change the way maintenance, reliability, and operations does their job. No longer are these teams looked at as just a fixed cost, but rather as this dynamic cost that can go up and down. Again, it's dependent on why people do what they do and how well they do what they do.

Now, you have a measure of people's abilities, and a maintenance technician isn't treated like just any other maintenance technician.

Unlike stand-alone software, a point solution, or a onetime employee campaign, asset operations is not just a new, corporate program-of-the-month, a knee-jerk reaction to an immediate problem, or fancy technology with bells and whistles. It's an entire shift in the mindset of how manufacturing, distribution, and other asset-intensive companies work all together. It's an abundant life cycle that reaches and affects every employee and each corner of the business.

Why AOM Is Needed

In just about every modern industry today, companies are facing this dynamic of a shortage of trained, skilled, and motivated workers coupled with increasing demands from customers and growing complexity from the technology and data now available.

This is no different for asset-intensive businesses. Over the last few decades, manufacturing has experienced a labor shortage, fueled even more so by the global COVID-19 pandemic and the Great Resignation. At the same time, technology demands a new level of skill and expertise, leading to an even greater demand for employees capable of not only using and applying solutions but maximizing and optimizing their capabilities. A host of statistics report that millions of jobs are expected to remain unfilled in upcoming decades and that recruiting and retention will remain as high priorities in the future as a result.

Asset-intensive companies will need to find innovative ways to attract and retain a skilled, talented, and motivated workforce to succeed. One of the underlying goals of AOM is that every team—and every employee—feels better supported, valued, and part of the company. Employee motivation and loyalty must be fostered at a whole new level, and AOM provides part of that solution.

The Cost of the Status Quo

Let's think about a fictitious business that operates dozens of machines as it packages and distributes infant food products. Although a few assets are relatively new, most are refurbished or used pieces of equipment and require regular repairs and maintenance.

The company recently grew large enough to justify a maintenance team of three, as well as a reliability engineer, all tasked with the goal of maximizing production by reducing downtime. The maintenance team uses an antiquated work order system that functions just above the old manual, paper-based system.

Employees start their mornings off at home by checking their news feeds, ordering groceries to be delivered when they return home that night, texting their child's coach, and confirming a doctor's appointment—all on their phones. Their navigation system automatically routes them around construction, accidents, and traffic to bring them to their workplace as quickly and efficiently as possible.

Yet, when technicians arrive, they punch an old-fashioned time clock; head to an antiquated workstation to see work orders for the day; grab files, a clipboard, and tools and begin their first task. Many are inwardly frustrated with the step back-in-time. They experience the difference technology can make in their personal lives; they know at some level that there must be a better way to operate at work as well.

With this underlying discontent, the first technician returns to a piece of equipment that she has worked on multiple times in the past year, making the same repair she always makes. She knows most likely there's an underlying problem, but there's no incentive to share that information and no place to record the issue. She simply executes the work order and marks it as complete and moves to the next task.

A second technician is relatively new and unfamiliar with the task at hand. The work order is unclear about the problem and does not contain all the details needed to completely understand the issue. He makes a few adjustments, based on his limited knowledge and training. He sends a quick text to his supervisor, who offers a few suggestions, but that conversation is not recorded. He completes the task, still uncertain that the issue has been truly resolved, but knows any resulting problems will surface in a future work order. He shrugs and moves on.

At the end of the day, the technicians must reserve time to enter the completed work orders into the system at a desktop computer. This information is stored, but infrequently accessed because the complex and confusing reports don't provide true business insights. They are diligently printed, glanced at, and often filed, never to be accessed again.

Meanwhile, the reliability engineer is looking at other data stored in the company's ERP system. This information reveals some issues, but work order data is not integrated. As a result, the engineer frequently makes changes and decisions that do not take into account the whole picture and may seem disconnected from maintenance.

The maintenance manager and technicians feel the stigma of being a necessary cost center, always under pressure to reduce costs and increase efficiency. Technicians feel like cogs in a machine and believe no one in management values their expertise. They do not feel valued; they believe no one really listens to them. As a result, they choose not to share knowledge or solve problems—they simply do what's asked of them and go home. After some time, the job feels boring and mundane, so most begin looking for more fulfilling opportunities.

This common cycle leads to the fact that many asset-intensive companies end up turning over their entire workforce every four years, requiring significant training and onboarding time on a near constant basis.

The HR challenge keeps this company from expanding into new markets or having the resources needed to invest in the equipment that would rapidly fuel its growth.

AOM as the Foundation of an Abundant Life Cycle

The management team sees these systemic issues within the company and decides to fully embrace AOM. They understand they need to make a radical shift in how they work and treat their employees to reach their revenue and growth goals in a competitive market. Although they have some foundational pieces of technology, they know they need a purpose-built system to bring the company's teams and data to better inform business decisions.

PEOPLE NEED TO UNDERSTAND WHAT THEY'RE DOING AND WHY THEY'RE DOING IT.

-RAMESH GULATI

Companies must abandon the mindset of simply managing assets. Instead, all employees must begin thinking about how those assets and their utilization impact the entire business. The company must implement an infrastructure, work processes, and technology that provides full visibility across the entire life cycle to make this possible. In addition, a culture shift that values the expertise, input, and contributions of every employee must be fostered. By doing these things, maintenance, reliability, and operations teams will get a seat at the revenue table.

Let's begin by looking at the infrastructure of AOM, which must be designed for the way maintenance, reliability, and operations personnel work. An AOM system must track asset, cost, and revenue data in order to arm teams with tools powerful enough for complex, multi-team workflows. Instead of working in departmental silos with similar but disconnected goals, AOM pulls the entire company together into one team, all working toward a common goal and pulling in the same direction.

The technology implementation itself should not be a time-consuming, massive IT project. Instead, the tools themselves should be intuitive and simple to learn, adopt, and put into practice with minimal training. AOM should centralize data, pulling it in from both active and passive sources, and connect that data to executive, business-focused metrics. This centralized repository becomes the single source of truth for all employees to draw from, contribute to, and access on a day-to-day basis. Then, find an AOM solution with mobile capabilities, allowing technicians to not only access comprehensive information about the particular asset they are working on, but also an easy place to add data, knowledge, and questions based on their own interactions with the asset.

Let's return to the technicians introduced earlier. Since the first technician can now access asset information on her mobile device, she scrolls through the asset repair history and sees the pattern of repeated repairs. She thinks that there may be a correlation to another piece of equipment nearby that periodically releases a great deal of heat. She makes a note of her hypothesis on her device and pings the reliability engineer, who can then investigate root causes further before another breakdown or a complete failure occurs.

The second, newer technician now has manuals, checklists and FAQs about the equipment at his fingertips on his mobile device. He recalls some of his training, easily looks up common issues with the asset, and learns more about the issue as he considers the problem. He can message his manager in real-time from his device with a few questions and make his repair, more confident that he has truly resolved the issue.

As equipment is better maintained and more efficiently repaired, the company sees downtime drop and productivity improve. All team members feel they have played a role in the result, utilizing the skills and training they have to the fullest. They are appreciated and rewarded for their efforts and seen as key contributors to the company's overall success and growth.

Improving the Culture

Morale was low when Michael Moran was asked to take over facilities management at Jewish Adoption and Foster Care Options (JAFCO). "Guys were almost ready to leave; they didn't feel appreciated, and they didn't feel like they were in the loop as far as what they were supposed to do," Michael recalled. Maintenance technicians used to sit around looking at social media on their phones when there was work to be done. Throughout the week, team members would be waiting for Friday when they'd be done with work.

Additionally, poor response time and organization caused reduced trust in the technician team. Michael thinks that listening to his technicians and believing in them was what caused the change. "There was an investment made in them," he said. "We believed in them enough to adopt a system that makes sense." Technicians started getting very specific, directed information, so they were actually able to accomplish tasks.

"I think the positive reinforcement of checking something off when it's done also makes you proud of what you're doing," said Michael. "And the guys working here don't sit around. They're always watching for work orders, and when they come in, they're ready to jump on it and get it done."

On the flipside, Michael made sure team members were recognized for their efforts. One of his teammates was promoted to supervisor and got a significant raise. Others also got raises and some extra time off as a bonus for the high productivity level.

STATE OF THE INDUSTRY

Ramesh Gulati

Maintenance Expert in Residence | *UpKeep*

Maintenance has been known as a necessary evil in most organizations, and those team members never get recognition for what they do. Granted, things have started to change lately, mainly because some of my colleagues and I have started talking so much about it. When we say maintenance is a cost center, it means something as a cost to the company or the organization. That's the wrong way of thinking. But now, I see maintenance has changed; it's being recognized and valued. And especially today, organizations are ISO certified. Each ISO standard requires a company to show how they're making improvements, and how all the parts are working together as one entity for the common goal. And to help with that, the companies reduce costs, but they also have to show they're all working together for a common goal. And maintenance plays a key role in that.

Competitive pressure, respecting the customer requirements—all these things are happening and putting pressure on the leadership of an organization to break down the silos. In any one organization, you need to work together with a common goal. And if you don't do that, you can't make people happy—your customers, stakeholders, as well as the people who make the things. And that's very important.

People are starting to work together more, and organizational structure is changing. In the past, most companies have had an operational department, production department, IT—all these different, separate departments are there. But now the organizational structure is changing. Where I worked for 25 years, and some of the organizations I've worked with, we were similar. But then we realized, "That's not holding water in a new organization." And so we decided to change our organizational structure. We said, "Hey, there's a person who's responsible for a small area, and they're responsible for all the assets." They're an asset manager. Now, they have responsibility and budget for all operations, production, capital improvements, everything in this area. We did this with several small operations, ensuring the asset manager had all the responsibility they needed to execute their duties.

Data collection is important for this. If you don't have good data coming out, that creates a problem because then you don't know what you're doing. Companies have to make a quality product, and to make quality products, they have to make sure the equipment is working properly, appropriately, and that it's not being misused. By misused, I mean not training or educating the operators; they're overburdened and stressed.

So, you have to keep your asset properties maintained, and all three departments have to work together. The way I look at any digital system is that its major function is being a data repository. In the front of that, there's data input to the system. So, you have to make it easier for people to do so and ensure the data quality is good. In many organizations, people are close to retiring and scared of computers. What we had to do was provide a data person to each area. The data people would work with the old timers to get the data, talk to them, and show them the right way to input data into the system. We realized those workers were scared to input the data; they didn't want to deal with it. Now, younger workers are much easier; they can go on the phone, etc.

So things are changing, but we still have to make sure data input is right. I'll give you an example: Once we had a heating furnace, and we had to make sure the temperature was a certain degree for our requirements. We later learned that after material was going into the furnace, it wasn't heating properly. We found out that we had to put the temperature sensor inside the furnace, and once we started taking data that way, we started finding out that some of our sensors weren't working right.

People need to understand what they're doing and why they're doing it. If they don't understand, they may not realize the value or objective of reaching company goals, especially if you want to bring about change. Change is improvement, but what's in it for me? Why do I have to change my habits?

I'll give you an example. A few years ago, I was somewhere renting a car. I got the car and started driving it. Suddenly, I realized my dashboard was missing. What the manufacturers did was move the dashboard from behind the wheel to the center. The reason they did that was because many countries drive on the opposite side of the road. So they put it in the center, so one could change the steering wheel to be on the left or right side, but the dashboard stays in the same place.

But driving with the dashboard in the middle was a challenge for me. I was looking straight, then turning right to see what speed I was going, always moving my neck. It was a big change. The car's design team never realized how me, the customer, was going to perceive it. They made a change and didn't ask me. Likewise, in a plant setting, you need to take the advice of your operators and maintainers when you want to make improvements. If you don't do that, you're not utilizing those people's entire knowledge and experience, and that's what's important.

I don't like the word maintenance. It has a negative connotation. People think it's somebody in the back of the room being given money just to fix things. So, I've been proposing that maintenance should be called capacity assurance. Give it a more positive spin. Maintenance isn't just maintaining something when something breaks, they're long-term maintaining that capacity in the asset or department. That's why maintenance, reliability, and operations have to work together to maintain that capacity.

CHAPTER 8

EVERYTHING MEASURED CAN BE IMPROVED

Imagine a world where you're constantly improving upon a base foundation layer and getting exponentially better—in your production, in your maintenance practice, in the future reliability of your equipment. You're taking all these learnings from before and applying them to today. Imagine that world. What could you do?

You can only improve what you measure. This is an old adage of the business world; and can be applied to just about any function in any industry. Why is it so often repeated? Although it seems like such a basic, foundational concept, it often gets lost in the day-to-day minutia of tasks, meetings, and urgent requests from internal or external customers.

When it comes to asset operations management, however, the core of that old adage becomes one of the eight pillars of success because so many of the improvements required in this system have a direct impact on the life and performance of critical assets themselves. These assets, in turn, affect the performance of the entire manufacturing company, its production capacity, and its all-important uptime metrics.

The Risks of Poor Measurement

Let's think about a medical supply company that manufacturers safety equipment for nursing and long-term care facilities. This organization runs critical assets over one shift and employs a single maintenance technician and a reliability engineer. Although the technician is extremely organized and responsive, no existing system records the work they perform on an ongoing basis. As a result, all the company's asset history resides in this individual's head. Not only does this make measurement of KPIs impossible, it is also a significant risk factor for the company if this individual chooses to leave.

The reliability engineer, on the other hand, pulls data that resides on the company's ERP system to analyze root causes of failures. Yet, this information is incomplete because maintenance data on assets is not included. Much of this data is also historic, making it difficult to address problems in a timely manner.

The Shift to AOM

The first step that this company takes to get a better handle on its existing data is to implement a mobile solution that can not only capture existing asset information and maintenance activities, but also fully integrate to the company's ERP and other back-end systems. The data captured by this solution must flow into a single repository, along with all the other data generated within the organization, both passively and actively, so that better measurement metrics can be identified and employed.

WE NEED ASSETS THAT ARE RELIABLE,
HAVE A HIGH MEAN TIME BETWEEN FAILURES,
HAVE A LOW MEAN TIME TO REPAIR,
AND ARE SAFE TO OPERATE.

-RAMESH GULATI

The most important aspect of setting measurement metrics is that they tie directly to overall business goals, such as percentage of downtime or revenue growth, not just simply measure activity. This can be a difficult mindshift for many companies, especially where employees are used to being rewarded for activity such as the number of work orders completed.

However, if the cultural shift can be made successfully and all employees can rally around business-focused metrics, team members tend to rise to the challenge of not only completing a to-do list, but getting behind the overall health and performance of an asset, which will directly affect the company's bottom line.

Time, Cost, and Efficiency Benefits

By selecting and integrating the best solutions, Certarus, low carbon energy solution company, has realized significant cost and time savings, as well as enormous gains in efficiency.

"Since we have real-time data, we're able to hold our team more accountable for work orders to be completed on time," said Kyle Dunbar, Fleet Maintenance Manager at Certarus. "We've saved so much time because we no longer need to figure out where equipment is located. Our people really like having that visibility to know where they're at during any given time."

Furthermore, the integrated system has allowed the company to better allocate its resources. Besides not wasting time trying to track down equipment, Certarus can now get to work orders faster, avoid unnecessary maintenance, and increase the utilization of its equipment.

"That all trickles down to dollars and cents at the end of the day," said Chi Fang, Manager of Technology & Business Process at Certarus. "When we look at all our integrations, which cost us a little more than $10,000, we think we're going to save about $50,000 per year. That's a 50-fold per year return on investment, which is really incredible by any measure. I think that those cost savings will only continue to grow as the size of our fleet grows."

STATE OF THE INDUSTRY

Ramesh Gulati

Maintenance Expert in Residence | *UpKeep*

Asset performance is essential in a plant, factory, or service provider company to deliver value for an organization. In the past, we've focused on optimizing maintenance to reduce failures and costs. However, in the last few years, we've learned that asset performance depends a lot more on other phases of the asset life cycle, including how assets are designed, built, installed, and commissioned.

The asset life cycle is important, as is the impact of design, procurement, installation, commissioning, and operations and maintenance (O&M) phases on total life cycle costs. It has been documented at many organizations that errors and omissions introduced during the design, build, and installation phases can increase both failure rates and O&M costs, thereby increasing total asset ownership costs.

Asset Life Cycle Phases

Assets—ranging from a piece of equipment to the whole plant/factory—have four key stages in their life cycle.

- ▶ **Need:** A need for the asset is established to provide a service or to make a product.

- ▶ **Acquisition:** An asset is designed, built, purchased, installed, and commissioned.

- ▶ **Utilization:** As the asset is operated, maintained, and improved to provide a service or to make a product.

- ▶ **Disposal:** The need is over, and the asset is decommissioned and disposed of.
  (Note: for the sake of simplicity, the term asset will be used for the assets or the plant/factory.)

The majority of the cost occurs in the utilization (operational) phase, where the asset is actually utilized, producing something. Depending on the type of asset, this phase may last for five years, 20 years, 50 years, or even more than 80 years. The other significant cost occurs in the acquisition phase.

However, typically we don't do a good job of identifying what we need and how much it will cost. Budgets are allocated too often as a part of capital projects and at a very high level, based on guesses. These budgets are then cut, resulting in an unreliable asset that costs a lot more during the operation phase. Generally, we also don't do a good job of projecting the impact of failures when justifying the higher acquisition costs and are forced to accept these cuts.

The Acquisition Phase, Explained

The acquisition phase generally consists of the following subphases:

- Specifications
- Design
- Purchase
- Build
- Install/Commission

This phase is very important in the asset life cycle. Working with many organizations has shown that we don't do a good job in this phase. Some of the reasons I've found are:

1. We don't do an adequate job of writing requirements and specifications. Either we don't know what we need, or we don't do a good job of explaining what and why we need something.

2. Budgets are cut from the top, either without explanation or because we haven't provided a reasonable justification for keeping RAMS[2]-related (reliability, availability, maintainability, safety, and sustainability) requirements. Generally, we're forced to keep the same production capacity in our requirements. However, to manage budget cuts, we sometimes settle for cheap and lower-reliability components, with no redundancy and sufficient spares. We might lack appropriate devices to monitor asset conditions or bypass rotating machines' proper alignment during installation/commissioning.

3. Training of O&M workforce is cut to a minimum or eliminated. We're advised that this could be done after assets are installed, which is not a good practice.

4. O&M manuals, drawings, and other documentation are delayed or provided in a preliminary stage. Many times, redline drawings are not updated after installations.

These are examples of issues facing O&M personnel when the capital budgets are cut. However, if we do the right things in this phase—maybe spending a little more money—the asset's reliability and safe operation will be improved. This results in higher uptime (fewer failures) and lower the total cost of ownership during the asset's life cycle. These are lessons we learned in the last few years, as have many other experts in this field, as reported and discussed in several recent reliability and asset management conferences.

Implementing Reliability Excellence

We have to ensure that we design, procure, build, and install assets with RAMS[2] principles. It's not easy to do that. It requires a lot of extra effort, coordination, and understanding of reliability principles, as well as creating the right culture involving all of the stakeholders. In this journey, the stakeholders who must ensure that we do the right things during the asset life cycle include:

- Asset owner
- Operational manager/engineer
- Capital project manager/engineer
- Design engineer
- Reliability engineer
- Maintenance manager/engineer
- Operations/process engineer
- Operators: technician
- Maintainer: technician
- Planner
- Procurement professional/officer
- Quality manager/engineer
- Human resources

All of these stakeholders are needed to create the right culture. Continuous engagement of all the stakeholders in doing the right things is essential during the asset life cycle.

We need assets that are reliable, have a high mean time between failures, have a low mean time to repair, and are safe to operate. Simply achieving this goal is a challenging task. Sustaining that goal is another challenging task but also achievable. It requires a culture of excellence—reliability excellence. It means all the stakeholders are engaged all the time. Also, it means that the stakeholders are aware of the industry's best practices and implement them effectively.

During the acquisition phase of the asset, when we are writing specifications, designing, procuring, building/constructing, and installing/commissioning the asset, we have ample opportunities to implement best practices. These practices would make the asset more reliable and safe to operate during the utilization phase. In addition, they will reduce the total cost of ownership for the entire life of the asset.

CHAPTER 9

DATA ACCESSIBLE FROM WHEREVER YOU ARE

Imagine working in a world where data is accessible from wherever you are. Everything, like your maintenance records, asset purchase price, inventory, labor hours, fuel costs, electricity, all in one single place.

This access would enable teams to look at the business holistically across the entire board. Any single, small change they make would be able to be connected to the impact it has on the bottom line. Additionally, it would change businesses from looking at every decision with a subjective view—what feels good, etc.— to a hard return on investment (ROI) conversation, where they can say with confidence whether or not they should make this decision, investment, repair, or run a piece of equipment to failure.

Having data accessible from anywhere would completely transform the way companies make decisions because now they would have data to back up all their decisions with confidence.

It would also change the way maintenance, reliability, and operations teams communicate with one another and make decisions. No longer would these teams be operating in a mindset of, "I think this is the right thing to do;" it would transition them into a mode of, "I know this is the right thing to do. Here's all the data, this is why." And it would ultimately help align all three teams.

Inaccessible Data Means Unreliable, Inefficient Businesses

Let's think about what's happening inside manufacturing facilities today. Although some companies have successfully moved away from pen and paper systems to a digital solution, many technicians are still inefficient because they're engaging with a desktop-based platform. Work orders are automatically entered and approved through the system; however, technicians must obtain their schedules at desktop computers or kiosks before heading to the location of the repair or task. Once work orders are completed, data must be recorded at these same fixed locations, which may lead to incomplete or forgotten information.

The reality is many software solutions are still desktop-based. This issue presents an access barrier, as the majority of maintenance, reliability, and operations professionals are not desktop-based. All the data, tools, and solutions in the world are limited or even useless if the employees who need them cannot tap into them on demand. Technology needs to be mobile, with an easy-to-use interface that's accessible in the field every minute of every day.

Some businesses have implemented incentives for technicians to record work orders correctly, completely, and in a timely fashion, which has helped improve the quality of the collected data. However, this data remains siloed from the purchasing software, which may have been integrated with the company's inventory management system. Although the chief operating officer (COO) has visibility into maintenance, repair, and operations (MRO) supplies and the purchasing department receives notifications when certain shortages are reached, these inventory levels are not integrated with data from work orders. As a result, there is likely a delay between the time a technician notes a need for tools or replacement parts and when that data becomes visible in the inventory system.

This barrier is a common scenario in many manufacturing organizations: the data explosion has resulted in unorganized, siloed, and inaccessible information. When data is locked within department silos, those who need the information cannot see it, resulting in inefficiencies, data gaps, and rework. It also leads to multiple and inaccurate understandings of the current state of each critical asset, depending on which pair of departmental glasses an employee is wearing.

This inaccurate view, combined with differing departmental objectives, often results in misaligned teams, misunderstood assets, and undersupported, frustrated employees.

For example, a maintenance technician may report a needed part for a machine, only to be notified a week later that it has been ordered. This delay results in downtime, drawing the COO's unwanted attention. It also results in an aging work order, affecting the technician's performance rating, even though there is no fault on the part of the technician. Meanwhile, the reliability team is exploring the cause of the problem in the first place, which may not be resolved by the part's replacement.

IF TEAMS KEEP OPERATING IN SILOS, THEY'RE GOING TO START DOING THINGS THAT AREN'T NECESSARY, SUCH AS OVER-MAINTAINING OR EVEN UNDER-MAINTAINING.

-GEORGE PARADA

When expanding this idea to include the fact that assets encompass not only equipment, but all the vital building blocks of experiences and other components of commerce, it's easy to see why organizations that fail to anchor their entire operating philosophy are bound to be unreliable.

If software solutions and siloed departments are charged with addressing a single aspect or area without a mission-critical, company-wide focus, inefficiencies and frustrations arise and affect the long-term performance of the organization.

The Key to Unlock Improved Workplace Operations

The goals of a purpose-built AOM solution are to manage multilocation daily maintenance life cycles; optimize asset utilization; and provide insights into real-time performance data. For maintenance, reliability, and operations teams, they gain a single, user-friendly tool that drives efficiency and effectiveness across the company.

An organization is primed to take all the quality work it has done and push it to the next level. In doing so, it breaks its cycle of undersupporting and undervaluing these three teams. Now, an organization is ready to launch the company into future efficiency and success.

On top of that, after implementing AOM, a company can accelerate the speed and quality of answers to questions across the organization, helping operations teams gain efficiency, as well as make smarter business decisions. Because obstacles to proactive maintenance are removed through AOM, operations teams can better plan their tasks to be productive each and every day.

With a single source of truth accessible anywhere, operations teams see the same accurate and comprehensive data that maintenance and reliability teams see, providing a granular level of detail for each asset interaction. This leads to enhanced and optimized performance. This central knowledge base ties together all fragmented systems, extending the value of current technologies.

As teams initiate a regular proactive maintenance strategy, they successfully reduce equipment downtime and achieve the full useful life of assets for operations. By anticipating replacement parts needed, AOM provides management with real-time notifications of part quantities.

The operations team now has a single operational blueprint for its company with efficient workflows and complete visibility, both key facets in improving workplace operations.

STATE OF THE INDUSTRY

George Parada
Global Asset Management Quality & Reliability Manager | *Meta*

I've seen maintenance, reliability, and operations teams in disconnected silos across the many different industries I've been a part of, or with people I've interacted with. And I'll be honest, it comes down to defined roles and responsibilities. What I mean by that is, it's important to understand who owns the assets and then who owns the capability of those assets. At the end of the day, maintenance, reliability, operations—they're all trying to do the same thing, trying to make sure those assets don't go down and that they meet their intended reliability targets or operational objectives.

But part of the problems that I've seen, and why we operate in silos, is that we don't have those requirements well defined around who does what to manage the ownership and capability of the asset. So, to me, operations owns the asset; the reliability team owns the capability of that, along with the maintenance teams.

If teams keep operating in silos, they're going to start doing things that aren't necessary, such as over-maintaining or even under-maintaining. Let me give you an example. When team interaction isn't defined, then teams are just creating data that's not going to even be utilized to leverage future decisions. They're going to have these recurring failures and operations is going to be complaining about it. But then reliability says, "Hey, we have a function we can play where we can rightsize what that maintenance strategy needs to be based off of failure analytics and things like that." So, again, it comes back to defined roles and responsibilities to prevent silos from continuing to grow.

When I think about the scattering of data, it's because we're collecting a lot of great information, but we're not putting it in a way where it can be presented visually. If I can tell a story then we can actually take action on what the data is.

What problem are you trying to solve? Who needs to notice information? If you can't answer those questions, or the results from the data/analysis aren't telling you, then why are you even measuring it? So it's important to not only think about the why but specifically, what's the what and how it's solving the problem. You have to keep it to very select things that you're going to measure because I've also seen a dashboard where they're measuring one hundred things. So does that mean we're taking one hundred or more actions on these things we're looking to measure?

I heard this quote from a conference once that really stuck with me. The guy was telling me that he was hired for a continuous improvement role, and he said, "Hey, build me a dashboard." So someone built him a dashboard and it contained over eighty different things. And the manager there immediately told him, "By showing me everything, you've shown me nothing."

What are those five things that when you walk the shop floor; talk to an operator, maintenance person, or supervisor—they know it. These are the five things I'm driving and how I'm trying to get them back into the green.

If a new initiative is going to be integrated into the company culture, it needs to always be tied into what the broader goals and objectives of the company are. If we're talking about a reliability initiative, an asset operations life cycle one—whatever it is, how does it tie into what the mission of the company is? We have to make that connection and ensure those people at the top are also referencing why these things are important. That way it's not just the reliability or operations teams that are trying to push it up and push it down. I know sometimes people struggle with top-down approaches, but as companies and industries scale, we need to have a consistent way around how we manage two expectations.

At the end of the day, people want to know what value these initiatives provide to them. I know a lot of companies struggle with that because you hear people talk about reliability, trying to solve for things that were never even supposed to happen in the first place, and how do you measure that? So that's why it's important to define upfront what problems you're trying to solve and how you're seeing the trends. Again, it goes back to the earlier example about leveraging data. We probably only need to look at five areas instead of five hundred areas to ultimately focus on what this does to the bottom line.

CHAPTER 10

MAINTENANCE, RELIABILITY, AND OPERATIONS ARE REVENUE DRIVERS, NOT COST CENTERS

Maintenance, reliability, and operations are often seen as necessary evils by most businesses, and some companies would even choose to forego those three teams if they could. These companies put up with these teams because they *have to*, or someone told them they should, or they've heard "You'll pay the price for it later." In that sense, companies have been conditioned to think of maintenance, reliability, and operations as an expensive cost prevention tool and insurance policy for all the assets that generate revenue for the business.

This perspective, however, creates conflict. For example, operations and maintenance teams tend to clash often. There's an inherent challenge where one team wants to keep things running for the day's productivity and revenue, while another team wants to shut the production line down for maintenance and longevity. Two different sides of the same coin. Is it ever possible to get them to meet?

Maintenance, Reliability, and Operations Are Investments

Most businesses don't see maintenance, reliability, and operations as a revenue driver. By the same token, teams have misaligned goals, resulting in infighting. If businesses don't change their perspective now, they'll optimize for the wrong metrics and lose revenue.

If you dive into maintenance KPIs, you'll most likely find two things at odds. "Measuring Maintenance Effectiveness," a *Reliable Plant* e-newsletter article by Ralph D. Hedding, emphasizes that thirty percent of maintenance work hours should be spent on performing routine maintenance. Whereas the 2021 article, "30 Best Manufacturing KPIs & Metric Examples for 2021 Reporting" from *insightsoftware*, says operations should maximize uptime for revenue and production attainment. Naturally, revenue and production from assets are going to lessen the more time is spent on maintaining these assets and shutting them down for maintenance.

These goals seem to be at odds. The important question to answer now is: how much is that misalignment costing your company? The solution to misalignment is alignment.

Ground Teams With a North Star Goal

One way to create alignment is by producing a system of objectives and key results, also known as an OKR system. The OKR system has made waves in the tech industry, but has yet to ripple into the maintenance, reliability, and operations industry. The entire goal of this system is to align incentives through cascading goals that support one north star objective.

YOU CAN INCENTIVIZE PEOPLE FOR
THEIR KNOWLEDGE AND EXPERIENCE BY
REWARDING THEM TO SHARE IT.

-APRIL JOHNSON

Currently, most maintenance teams think of goals from the ground up. These teams measure preventive maintenance compliance, number of work orders completed, and mean time between failure as numbers to hit to signify successful maintenance. But doing that is celebrating inputs and not outcomes.

Establishing an OKR system flips this methodology on its head. The industry thinks of a singular goal and cascades from there. In this situation, maintenance teams measure on an objective like production, which is a top-down approach. Here, you celebrate outcomes.

By using this methodology, all teams within the company would be unified under a single north star goal, like production and revenue. From there, individual goals for different departments are set to reach the decided outcome. For example, a maintenance team is given goals, like tracking uptime versus downtime, while the operations team may be focused on measuring materials cost per unit produced.

In theory, all these goals should contribute in tandem to the overall objectives. If equipment is maintained, it should be consuming materials more efficiently. On the other hand, if one machine is consuming more than another, it's a signal that the maintenance team should inspect it and see what could be done to boost production. The takeaway here is these key results are measured based on how they're contributing to the overall goal. In an OKR system, no objective stands alone.

The Impact of North Star Goals

According to research by Detecon and the *Harvard Business Review*, the average company is expected to accrue a failed projects cost of $11.8 million per year, and millions in cost accrued from employee churn. Their research finds that this can be consistently alleviated by orienting goals around outcomes—alignment. When teams are not fighting over goals, these findings suggest that employees are happier, more productive, and retainment increases. In the process, this generates more revenue for your company.

If a team is aligned and heading on a path toward a single goal, then every single team/department understands the impact each has to reach that goal at the highest level. There's a compass now. Consequently, this also grants teams more autonomy and clarity to make tough decisions more efficiently.

Let's say a team finds out it has to sacrifice an hour of productivity for advanced employee training. If you're not measuring teams by their daily goal, it's easier for management to sacrifice that time, knowing it will contribute to their overall production north star goal for the year.

Trial and Error Is Key

One thing to keep in mind is that the OKR system requires consistent trial and error to test how each individual key result is contributing toward the greater whole. Maintenance, reliability, and operations teams will have to figure out this question: "How do we optimize short-term versus long-term goals?" You can't put all your eggs in one basket; it has to be somewhere in the middle.

That said, the OKR system is great for annual goals. The goal tracking lasts long enough where a team has a full year to build a plan, but it's also short enough where it's not stretched out over 10 years because who knows what curveballs could arrive.

Better Spare Parts Management Saves Thousands

One of the pain points that an American beverage company dealt with daily was that spare parts were not tracked and often got lost. The company found itself paying high expedited shipping costs when equipment broke down.

When parts needed to be ordered, they were just thrown on a credit card and never tracked. If the company had spare parts, nobody knew where they were or how many they had. When a machine would break, employees would have to order parts from Italy which would take weeks. Regularly, there were times when the lines would sit down for days or weeks while vendors rushed in parts.

After implementing AOM, spare parts are now ordered before they run out and can be located quickly. Spare parts are sitting on a shelf and team members know what they have and know what they need. Also, purchase orders are generated automatically.

It's been hugely helpful. There have been a number of times that something has gone off on the floor or broken down, and the company was able to get it resolved within 10 or 15 minutes because they had the part and knew where it was. When you consider that their average cost for downtime is $2,500 per hour per line, that's a huge savings.

Learn to Optimize

In hindsight, measuring maintenance based on how well maintenance teams can hit 100% preventive maintenance compliance, while measuring operations based on how well they can hit 99%+ uptime should have led companies to believe that conflict was inevitable. You can't have both. What teams *can* do is optimize. Set one goal for all teams to hit and let your quarterly/weekly/daily goals cascade from there.

Companies are too often celebrating the wrong things: the inputs and hours worked instead of the outputs and milestones achieved. Ultimately, what businesses should be focused on is celebrating the outcomes, like the output of critical assets. From there, the focus should be on optimizing the key results that lead to that.

It will be different for each team, but that's the point. The AOM system is a balancing act.

STATE OF THE INDUSTRY

April Johnson
Maintenance Manager | *PepsiCo*

Most of us have heard one variation or another of this story. It's the story where an old engineer/mechanic is called to work on a machine that had been down for some time and critical to get running. The experienced and knowledgeable mechanic inspects the machine briefly, pulls out a hammer, taps on the machine, and the machine begins running. When he invoices the company for his services, the company becomes upset because of the high cost of the invoice. The mechanic itemizes the invoice as usually one to five dollars, depending on the version of the hammer, and the rest of the invoice is usually in the thousands for knowing where to tap with the hammer.

This story is posted and published several times per year on social media, used in speeches at conferences, quoted as an example of quantity of work vs. quality of work, and used to encourage people with technical knowledge to not undervalue themselves. I understand the lessons in the story, and I am not going to tear down the value of knowledge and experience. Respect for work and knowledge of craftspeople is a foundation of any maintenance team. Personal ownership of equipment and processes is of great value to companies and teams.

But are there times when this can become toxic and dangerous to a company? And if so, how can you recognize the situation and actively prevent it?

Tribal knowledge is defined by iSixSigma as "any unwritten information that is not commonly known by others within the company. This term is used most when referencing information that may need to be known by others."

It's normal to have individuals who specialize in a piece of equipment or type of equipment. But when that specialization turns into an exclusive and hostile hoarding of information or resources, the team members, and ultimately the company, are at risk of being held hostage by that tribal knowledge. When information cannot be clearly shared and documented for the entire team, a company is put at a disadvantage. Training, improvement, and standardization opportunities are slim to none. If the person holding the information were to become unable or unwilling to work, the team is left scrambling trying to pick up the pieces on equipment they are unfamiliar with.

In my first leadership role, I encountered a mechanic who went to great lengths to ensure that no one but him knew how to work on the equipment in one area. He locked all of the original equipment manufacturer (OEM) manuals in his toolbox, kept the parts for the area hidden in secret hiding places all over the plant, and was confrontational if he saw anyone near "his" equipment. He even went as far as to lock out the machinery when he was not going to be in the plant, and if the line wasn't running, no one could touch the machine when he was not present.

Since no one could work on anything in the area but him, he was on call 24/7 and was making more than anyone else in the plant due to after-hour call-ins and overtime. The rest of the team were highly discouraged by his behavior and demoralized that he could get away with these things for so long. Probably even more shocking to me was how the other departments believed that he was the "best" on the team because if anyone else ever had to work in the area, they looked confused, could never find the parts or manual, and ended up calling him at home. To the people who didn't understand what was going on, he was a hero and was often recognized with gift cards and praise for coming in "whenever he was needed" to keep the plant productive.

When I confronted him about this behavior, he explained to me that this was "job security," and that "we could never lay him off or fire him." He did this intentionally, and by doing this, he had "made himself indispensable." The three things I found the most puzzling about the situation were:

1. The company had allowed it to get as far as it did.

2. There were people, including the plant manager, who agreed that no one should touch the machine but him. (Because when others had tried, "it hadn't worked out well.")

3. He had let fear and selfishness drive him to the point of sabotaging the rest of his team.

While I wish I could say that I got through to him with countless coaching sessions, asking him to train others, telling him that his "job security" could come from being a subject matter expert and guiding the rest of the team, eventual verbal and written write ups, etc. in the end, he did not change his ways and we parted ways. Since then, I have seen varying degrees of this behavior in other individuals. Here are some ways to combat tribal knowledge.

Build a Department Mission and Vision Statement

If possible, include teamwork, knowledge sharing, or some variation of this and rally the team behind it. Set the expectation up front.

Create a Safe Environment

While you may not be able to control outside influences, like market trends and company decisions for layoffs, you do control the type of environment within your work team. Create an environment where people are shown respect, empathy, concern, and where teamwork is expected, so people will be less likely to hold information.

Encourage Information Sharing by Sharing Information and Soliciting Feedback

In the new high turnover workforce, many seasoned veterans have worked for so many managers and leaders that they don't see the need to invest in your success by helping you out. The remedy is to deeply invest in their success. Share all information you can about the future, budgets, vision and mission, and solicit feedback. Really listen to what is being said.

Stop Rewarding Behavior That You Don't Want Repeated

It sounds simple enough, but it happens. Reward proactive activities. Reward knowledge sharing. Reward documenting a process or procedure. Reward creating troubleshooting guides. You can incentivize people for their knowledge and experience by rewarding them to share it.

Complete Audits on Preventive Maintenance or Routine Work

Auditing the work that is being done can be eye-opening for all involved. While auditing a written job procedure with a mechanic who was retiring, 20 additional tasks he completed that were not documented were identified. When asked about it, he said he hadn't printed the procedure in years because he had been doing it for so long. Those critical tasks, if we had missed documenting them, would have caused us problems had we not caught them.

Use Technology to Transfer Knowledge

Use smart glasses, video, photos, data collection, AOM, accurate work order information, purchasing records, problem descriptions, causes and remedies in work orders, root cause analysis, and problem-solving information. Don't just ask for people to be trained, but create multimedia training materials.

Include OEMs and Vendors When Available

Use outside resources to fill in the blanks and keep knowledge up-to-date.

PART 3

Implementing Asset Operations at Your Company

When you're ready to begin implementing AOM at your organization, here's a blueprint to do just that. Like any new initiative, the leadership team, accountability and reporting structures, and definition of responsibility will be key.

Because AOM is really a consolidation of existing technologies, processes, and initiatives, the implementation of this concept may be simply a reorganization and refinement of systems you already have in place so they work in concert with one another.

AOM is designed to bridge the silos between maintenance, reliability, and operations teams within asset-intensive businesses. Implementing AOM is about collecting asset data, analyzing insights, and driving actions to optimize the health and performance of your equipment. That should be the overarching vision of your AOM team.

CHAPTER 11

COMMON IMPLEMENTATION CHALLENGES

Organizations face a number of challenges when attempting to implement a new initiative. This chapter addresses the most common ones. It's helpful to know and recognize what these common challenges are so you can better understand and avoid them.

Software Complexity

The complexity of some legacy systems can make it difficult for your staff to use, and that makes training more challenging. In some cases, the learning curve can even foil deployment. Even with a user-friendly solution like AOM, there's still some training required to make sure the system is used correctly.

Additionally, oftentimes many of the software features aren't used, which can decrease the cost-effectiveness of the system. Statistics show that only about 6% to 15% of on-site CMMS users utilize their system to its fullest capacity.

Infrastructure Requirements

In order for AOM to flourish, the IT infrastructure in place needs to be able to support it. This could mean the IT network might need to be upgraded in order to support the features AOM provides. For example, AOM relies on an internet connection for much of its functionality. Without stable internet, the system won't be as reliable.

Also, intranet (connectivity within the facility) needs to be fast and stable. If the system proves sluggish, it can lead to user frustration, and can ultimately lead to your teams refusing to use it and reverting back to older methods.

Change Management

An effective change management process is essential to AOM implementation. Adding this system to your process can represent a change in the way the organization goes about its business. It is possible your staff may be resistant to that change. On top of ensuring the technical aspects of AOM implementation are handled correctly, the changeover process also needs to be conducted in a way to help everyone get on board.

Maintenance, reliability, and operations teams should be well informed about new processes, how they'll work, and what will be expected of them. If the implementation process isn't handled well, team members could lose faith in the system and opt for the old ways.

Planning

Planning is a vital part of AOM implementation, and one that can be easily missed. An AOM solution by itself won't fix a company's issues. In order to implement AOM properly, a company needs to create an action plan that includes what kinds of data to track, what functionality is needed, what the budget is, and stakeholder approvals and buy-in.

Implementation is more than just installing the software. It involves many critical factors that should be planned for. Factors like:

- ▶ How is data being migrated from previous systems?
- ▶ Is there an operational blueprint designed and ready to be scheduled?
- ▶ Has the software been tested in an area before being rolled out to the entire business?
- ▶ Is everyone communicating on the same page?

Training

When a new asset arrives at a facility, the relevant team members need to get trained on usage and tasks. It's the same idea with AOM. Training shouldn't be a one-time thing either. Continuous training is extremely important. When a business skimps on training, the staff won't know how to use the system that's supposed to make their lives easier.

Data

The data collection process can easily derail AOM. If you put garbage data in, you get garbage data out. Maintenance teams need to understand what kinds of data they need to input. Hands-on training can help with this. If workers are shown how to input useful, quality information, the data you get out will be more accurate.

CHAPTER 12

AOM IMPLEMENTATION BEST PRACTICES

Build Your Team

Begin by establishing and appointing an asset operations manager to lead the implementation, consolidate resources, and manage ongoing AOM efforts. This manager's central focus must be the optimization of your company's critical equipment and machinery. Although having experience in maintenance, operations, and reliability can be extremely useful in this position, it's important to make the shift from siloed departmental goals to the assets themselves.

This individual is responsible for defining key performance indicators (KPIs) for the team, managing the responsibilities and performance of each team member, and reporting results to the company's key stakeholders. The assets operations manager is also responsible for selecting and overseeing the implementation of the software, tools, and technologies required for AOM.

Depending on the size of your company and the number of assets you need to optimize, the next task is to define your asset operations team. Ensure that the whole team understands the vision of AOM—the optimization of each and every critical piece of equipment and machine.

The team should work together to create SMART goals that are specific, measurable, achievable, relevant, and time-bound. By doing so, all team members will understand how their individual performance will be judged, as well as the overall objectives of the team. Along the same lines, define KPIs and make sure you communicate progress against those KPIs on a regular and consistent basis.

The AOM manager should meet with each individual on the team to define that person's specific role and responsibilities, as well as to schedule and assign tasks. By using AOM software and systems to help track the progress and quality of their work, the manager can provide feedback, support, and professional development on a regular basis.

Select Universal KPI Metrics

Measuring the right things is one of the keys to a proper AOM implementation. Although there are a whole host of metrics that maintenance, operations, and reliability can measure, not all of them will be useful in understanding overall asset health or in making broader, asset-based business decisions. They can be used to measure progress toward a particular objective, but not necessarily as a final goal.

KPIs should be metrics that provide insight into the company's performance as a whole and should be tied to overarching business objectives. They are typically a specific number to hit for the entire organization.

Leading and lagging indicators are other ways to classify KPIs; the first predict future outcomes, while the latter looks at past performance.

Leading indicators are designed to lead to results. For instance, schedule compliance can be used to consider the likelihood of downtime by describing the amount of planned maintenance activities performed on time. It also can be used to look at maintenance activity effectiveness and how that will increase reliability.

Lagging indicators are the results of processes and operations themselves. For example, mean time to repair or mean time between failure can be measured to confirm trends that may have developed in a particular facility over time. They serve as a historical record, offering insight into which past events may be directly linked to a plant's performance.

In order to select the best KPIs to track for implementation of your asset operations management initiative, ask yourself the following questions:

What are our company goals?

It's critical to align AOM activities with overall company goals to ensure you're measuring the right things. For instance, a business that wants to increase production should measure some related maintenance activities to help reach availability targets.

Under that overall goal, you will want to establish related departmental targets. To increase production on a manufacturing line, the team may establish a metric that looks at a specific conveyor system's uptime and set a related goal to increase that uptime by a certain percentage by a specific date. Leading indicators to support that goal may include preventive maintenance as a percent of total maintenance, schedule compliance, and maintenance backlog.

What are we already tracking?

This question can be a bit of a double-edged sword. Some organizations may be wasting valuable time and resources tracking useless information or data that cannot fuel actionable change. To continue doing so would be counterproductive to AOM implementation. On the other hand, accumulating quality data takes time, and starting from scratch can delay the returns AOM promises to provide.

The key is to weigh the costs and benefits of tracking particular metrics and ensure they can play an active role in AOM. For example, if a company that wants to better understand its conveyor system is already tracking preventive maintenance, the AOM team can begin gleaning insights from existing preventive maintenance data. Trying to analyze things like schedule compliance would require time and resources to collect data first.

Before adding new KPIs, and the resources required to track and collect them, have a clear understanding of what you'll use the data for, what actions the data will drive, and how the information will help you better understand your business.

What types of assets are we tracking and are they critical?

This question helps you parse out which assets truly need to be tracked and the appropriate ways to do so. For example, mission-critical assets that play a key role in keeping your production lines up and running every day may require preventive maintenance, mean time to repair, and other such KPIs to ensure as much uptime and reliability as possible in terms of asset operations. Light bulb or office supply replacements, on the other hand, may demand simple tracking of inventory levels instead.

If the failure of an asset could lead to significant health, safety, environmental, and process problems, and if the chance of that failure is high, it will be more important to track leading indicators. Those assets that are more reliable and less disruptive may only need cursory checks of lagging indicators.

Remember that minor, chronic failures, even on less critical equipment, can cause major problems over time.

What are the cause-and-effect relationships?

Finally, it's important to select leading indicators in an AOM system that actually can impact overall goals and results. This may require some trial and error by setting leading indicators and then checking correlating lagging indicators at a later time. Check related studies for critical equipment to see if preventive maintenance tends to lead to reduced costs and unplanned downtime, and then fine-tune decisions about metrics to track.

Remember that selecting the right KPIs for AOM is about measuring the things that can help a company improve processes, plan business decisions, and boost overall performance.

Strive for Asset Operations Management Best Practices

To achieve success, an organization should strive toward best practices in asset operations management. Here is a list to use as a foundation:

- ▶ Link asset, maintenance, and reliability data to executive metrics such as revenue, cash conservation, and margin.

- ▶ Centralize data flow into a single command center to remove departmental silos and connect teams.

- ▶ Increase the visibility of analytics to improve and accelerate operations across the company.

- ▶ Standardize and document workflows to eliminate trial-and-error and inefficient communications.

- ▶ Change the culture by revising the conversation from questions like "How many hours did you work?" to "What value did you bring?"

- ▶ Automatically assign tasks to the appropriate team members that have the correct level of expertise.

CHAPTER 13

10 WAYS TO OVERCOME THE CHALLENGES OF AOM IMPLEMENTATION

It's only natural to come across bumps in the road to AOM implementation. But just because you encounter bumps doesn't mean there are no options when an AOM implementation project is going south. Here are 10 options to consider.

1. Scale Back

One of the biggest problems with AOM implementation is the speed at which organizations try to convert their entire operation. With this in mind, if AOM isn't being adopted by everyone, it's a good idea to take a step back and work out the kinks.

Gather specific feedback to understand why people don't want or don't know how to adopt the system. Scale back to one area and fix the problems there before moving on. Proving demonstrated implementation and its benefits in one area is a great way to both gather stakeholder buy-in and influence workers to use the system.

2. Gather Feedback

In tandem with the previous tip, feedback is extremely important to AOM implementation. If the system is failing to get off the ground, people probably aren't using it, don't know about it, or don't like it. You might be quick to dismiss these people, but they'll actually give you the most valuable feedback for the implementation process.

For instance, what seems simple on the platform might be difficult for the average employee. Perhaps training materials need strengthened, or maybe not enough employees know about it, so there's confusion amongst teams about which system is correct. Use this feedback to improve your process.

3. Seek Assistance

It's not always fun to ask for help outside your organization, but there are many useful resources that can help a failing AOM implementation gain strength. This is especially true if the people running the implementation don't have the level of maintenance, reliability, and operations knowledge to keep implementation moving forward.

4. Begin Focusing on Proactive Maintenance

Without a sound strategy, AOM will be little more than a work order management system in your organization. To be truly effective, you need to have a proactive approach to maintenance, reliability, and operations. When it comes to switching from a reactive to a proactive mindset, it's often best to take a gradual approach.

Departments should pick a key asset, determine some preventive or proactive task they should perform on it, and then start creating recurring work orders. As team members get used to the new routine, start rolling out the plan to other assets. Over time, your company's culture should start shifting to a proactive mindset.

5. Establish Clear Objectives

It's vital to know what you want to achieve with AOM. Some possibilities include:

- ▶ Reducing equipment breakdowns;
- ▶ Easing the administrative burden of preventive maintenance;
- ▶ Supporting predictive maintenance processes;
- ▶ Improving MRO inventory management;
- ▶ Tracking maintenance data.

Your objectives may include one or more of these, but it's important to make sure your goals are based on your organization's needs. In addition, you'll need plans for how these objectives will happen—keeping the functions of AOM in mind—and how to measure success.

When determining what objectives are best for your facility, consult with personnel at all levels, from your technicians all the way up to your maintenance manager. Additionally, people from other departments (e.g., IT, operations, etc.) should have some input as well. That way, nothing gets left out of the decision-making process.

Outlining these objectives will help you determine whether implementation is a success or not, and will also inform what kinds of modules you'll want to invest in.

6. Get an Implementation Process Together

The process of implementing AOM needs to be adequately spelled out, complete with timelines and milestones. Some key points to consider when creating your AOM implementation plan include:

- ▶ How data will be collected and inputted into the system.

- ▶ How IT infrastructure will be brought to standard.

- ▶ What hardware will be needed to support AOM and implementation objectives.

- ▶ What workflows your maintenance personnel and other employees will need to follow.

- ▶ What shape training will take.

- ▶ Who will perform each task.

- ▶ When each task will be completed.

It's important to make sure the whole organization is in on the implementation process, but it also helps to have one person who will spearhead the operation and help bring all other parties together.

7. Train on the Purpose of AOM

As you implement your new system, your personnel will need to be trained on how to use it. That means training them on how AOM is intended to support a holistic company strategy rather than act as a strategy unto itself. Illustrating the purpose of the system will help head off any misconceptions that may arise with respect to its intended usage.

It's also vital to get employee buy-in. By showing how AOM will make their jobs easier, you'll get the support you need in order to make sure they use the new software properly.

8. Consult the Software Provider

An AOM provider can offer plenty of support to help you get your new system off the ground. Consulting directly with the provider can help you determine which features are necessary to support your organizational goals, while also helping with the technical aspects of implementing the software into your existing processes.

Aside from their customer support, most providers offer instructional resources as well, which can be vital during implementation and throughout employee training.

9. Get Buy-In from All Levels

It's vital to get buy-in from all levels of your facility, from maintenance personnel to high-level executives. Training your employees on the purpose of AOM and illustrating how it can improve the workplace can help get employee buy-in, while illustrating the potential benefits of the software to senior-level managers and executives can get you the administrative support you need.

Ultimately, senior management provides the funding, while the entry-level staff will actually use the software and processes—just as long as they believe in it.

10. Work Where Your Employees Are

An easy-to-use and easy-to-implement software system will make the process much smoother and eliminate many of the obstacles that may impede implementation. An AOM system saves much of the hassle that clunky, legacy software often entails, ultimately improving the odds that implementation will be successful.

Looking Ahead

As you begin your journey into AOM, you will likely experience some resistance, especially if your maintenance, reliability, and operations teams have been working successfully as independent entities. Be sure to establish KPIs that answer the question, "What's in it for me?" for each of these functions so they can easily see how AOM will make their jobs easier and contribute to the overall success of the organization, their functions, and their individual careers.

Good luck on your AOM journey!

ABOUT THE AUTHOR

Ryan Chan is CEO and Founder at UpKeep. He is a Chemical Engineer from University of California, Berkeley and was named one of *Forbes* 30 Under 30 for Manufacturing in 2018. Ryan started UpKeep out of passion and frustration by the lack of mobility in today's maintenance management software. UpKeep has now been deployed to over 3,000 businesses and is a leader in mobile-first Asset Operations Management software.

Ryan brought UpKeep to life in 2015 from an idea he had while working as a process development engineer at a membrane manufacturing plant. He noticed that one of the biggest problems at the facility was the extremely cumbersome process of creating, keeping track of, and closing out maintenance work orders.

Whether it was a broken piece of equipment on the manufacturing line, a busted door lock, or a simple filter replacement, work orders would create stacks and stacks of papers that were easily lost and hard to prioritize. The team wasted a ton of time going back and forth from the production facility to the office multiple times a day so they could retype their notes into a desktop application.

Ryan realized that with modern cloud and smartphone technology, he could create an easier solution and save the maintenance team hours a day and a lot of lost uptime. With mobility in mind, he set out on a mission to drastically improve the workflow, and therefore productivity, of maintenance teams across the globe.

After thousands of hours, gallons of coffee, and lots of feedback, UpKeep had lifted off. Now, UpKeep is one of the most innovative products on the market and the first to approach maintenance management software from a mobile-first perspective. With UpKeep, workers can easily create work orders by simply snapping a picture, filling out a few fields, and sending it off to the maintenance department for repair — all from a mobile device. Over 400,000 users have already experienced the power of saving time and frustration with UpKeep and more are joining every day.

CONNECT & CONTINUE
THE CONVERSATION

Uniquely positioned to tackle industry challenges, UpKeep brings maintenance, reliability and operations teams together in a new approach called Asset Operations Management.

Asset Operations Management provides real-time data into the day-to-day maintenance life cycle, asset utilization, and performance measurement to support informed decisions that optimize maintenance strategies, improve asset performance, and increase availability and reliability.

Join us on our mission to share this new approach to maintenance and reliability. Learn more at **upkeep.com/aom**, or connect with us on social:

@on-upkeep

@onupkeep

@onupkeep

@upkeepaom

@onupkeep

You're also invited to join 5,000 maintenance and reliability professionals in UpKeep's Maintenance Community. This free, online forum provides networking in real-time, events, and tons of helpful resources on all things maintenance, reliability, and operations. Whether you're new to maintenance or reliability, or an industry veteran, there's always something to learn in The Maintenance Community.

Visit **upkeep.org** to join today!

Made in the USA
Columbia, SC
09 June 2022

61535664R00063